D0489802

Mensa
The High IQ Society
LOGIC
CHALLENGES

THIS IS A CARLTON BOOK

This edition published in 2017 by
Carlton Books
20 Mortimer Street
London W1T 3JW

Copyright © 2017 Carlton Books Limited

This book is sold subject to the condition that it shall not, by way of trade or otherwise, be lent, resold, hired out or otherwise circulated without the publisher's prior written consent in any form of cover or binding other than that in which it is published and without a similar condition, including this condition, being imposed upon the subsequent purchaser.
All rights reserved.

ISBN: 978-1-78097-917-5

Printed in Dubai

LOGIC CHALLENGES

TEST YOUR APTITUDE FOR DEDUCTION
AND EXAMINE YOUR IQ WITH 200 PUZZLES

CARLTON
BOOKS

What is Mensa

Mensa is the international society for people with a high IQ.
We have more than 100,000 members in over 40 countries worldwide.

The society's aims are:
to identify and foster human intelligence for the benefit of humanity
to encourage research in the nature, characteristics, and uses of intelligence
to provide a stimulating intellectual and social environment for its members

Anyone with an IQ score in the top two per cent of population is eligible to become a member of Mensa – are you the 'one in 50' we've been looking for?

Mensa membership offers an excellent range of benefits:
Networking and social activities nationally and around the world
Special Interest Groups – hundreds of chances to pursue your hobbies and interests – from art to zoology!
Monthly members' magazine and regional newsletters
Local meetings – from games challenges to food and drink
National and international weekend gatherings and conferences
Intellectually stimulating lectures and seminars
Access to the worldwide SIGHT network for travellers and hosts

For more information about Mensa: www.mensa.org, or

British Mensa Ltd.,
St John's House,
St John's Square,
Wolverhampton
WV2 4AH
Telephone: +44 (0) 1902 772771
E-mail: enquiries@mensa.org.uk
www.mensa.org.uk

Contents

INTRODUCTION

Puzzles are a staple part of the human condition. Every society on Earth knows of puzzles, and makes use of them for entertainment and education. Likewise, through history, every period we have reasonable archaeological or documentary data for shows evidence of puzzle use, even as far back as the ancient Babylonian civilisation. Curiosity and challenge are powerful motivators, as is the drive to compare our abilities to those of others. So it's no surprise that puzzles have established themselves so thoroughly.

Over the years, puzzles have taken many forms, from tests of manipulation right through to highly abstract mental reasoning. At its core, a puzzle is a test of analytical ability – if I am given a set of initial condititions X, then what is the correct way to find an end-state, Y. This is true whether Y is the solution to an equation, a plausible situation that could have led to X, or simply an understanding of what X means.

In this sense, many games can be seen as puzzles of a sort. In many one-on-one games, each move is in itself a small puzzle where the solution is to move towards victory. This is obvious in something like chess, but look at Sun Tzu's *The Art of War* and it becomes clear that even battle is, in many senses, a practical puzzle. Likewise, some stories are overt puzzles, such as Agatha Christie's work. But any tale can be something of a puzzle as the reader/listener attempts to gain understandings and form expectations.

Most of the puzzles we know from ancient civilisations are physical, things to fit together or disassemble or manipulate in some other way. It doesn't necessarily imply the absence of other types of puzzle, of course. It's just that solid objects tend to weather the centuries better than oral knowledge or written manuscripts. We can prove that mazes date back at least five thousand years, disentanglement puzzles around two thousand, and likewise tile puzzles such as tangrams and the ostomachion.

Written and spoken puzzles haven't survived the historical process so well. Scholars like Professor David Singmaster have put great effort into tracing the oldest evidence for various types of mathematical and logical puzzles, but there must be more material that has been lost. Perhaps, in time, some of it will be uncovered. We can only hope.

There is no need to mention here the pleasure to be gained from mastering a puzzle. Few people on the face of the planet have not experienced that glow from time to time. So let me just say that this book will give you plenty of opportunity to indulge yourself, secure in the knowledge that you are tapping in to one of the most persistent threads of human experience. The fact that exercising your brain can be shown to strengthen your faculties is just a fortunate extra benefit.

Happy puzzling!
Tim Dedopulos, London.

PUZZLES

01

Which two cubes show three identical faces to each other?

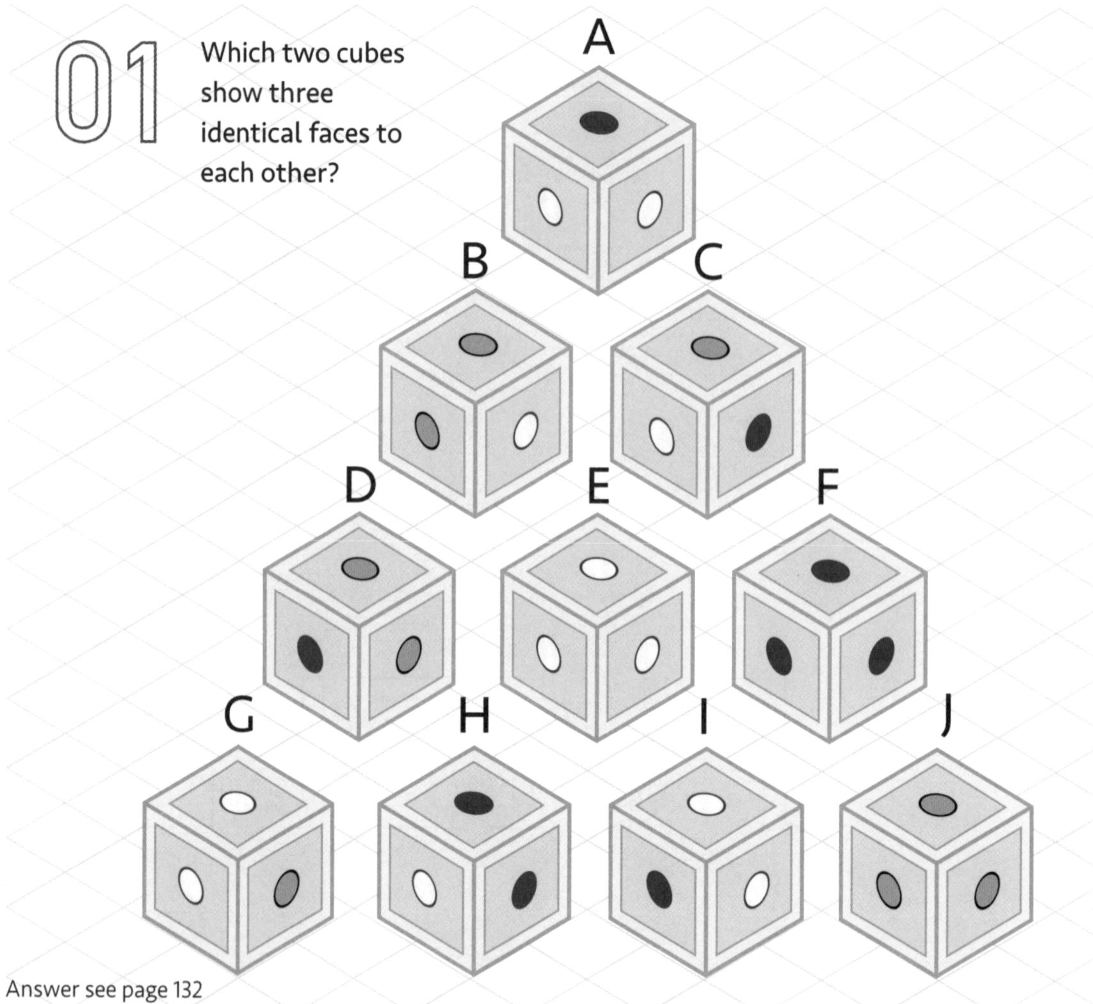

Answer see page 132

Answer see page 132

02

Fill in the missing plus, minus, multiplication, division, and/or factorial signs to make the equation below correct, performing all calculations strictly in the order they appear on the page.

21 11 18 5 15 21 4 = 59

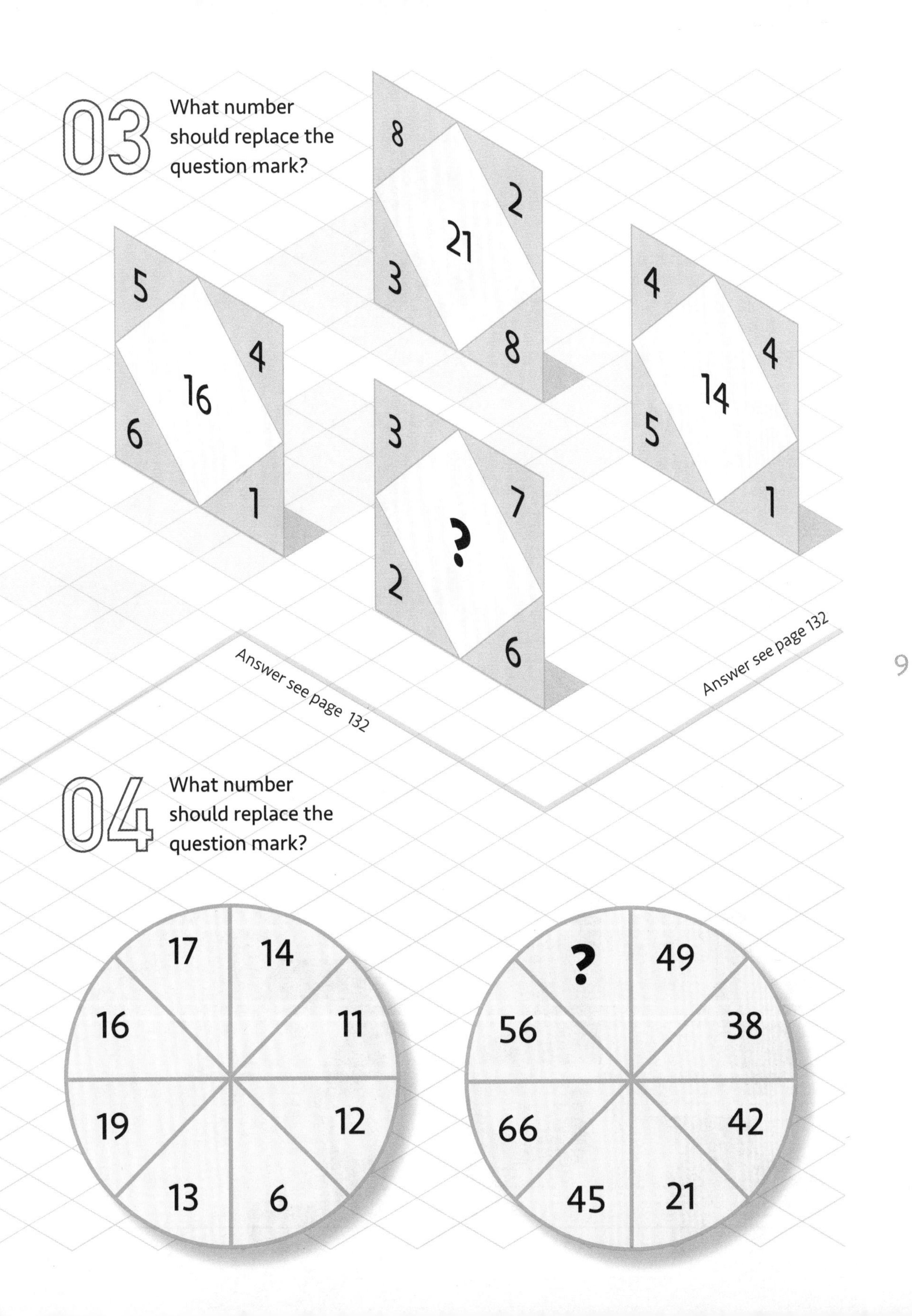
03
What number should replace the question mark?
8
2
21
3
8
5
4
16
6
1
4
4
14
5
1
3
7
?
2
6
Answer see page 132
Answer see page 132
04
What number should replace the question mark?
17
14
16
11
19
12
13
6
?
49
56
38
66
42
45
21

In the grid below, how much is each symbol worth?

13

10

14

9

15

6

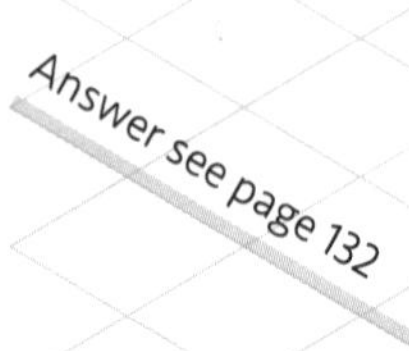

The pieces can be assembled into a regular geometric shape. What is it?

Answer see page 132

Decipher the names of several celebrities using the telephone dial as a guide.

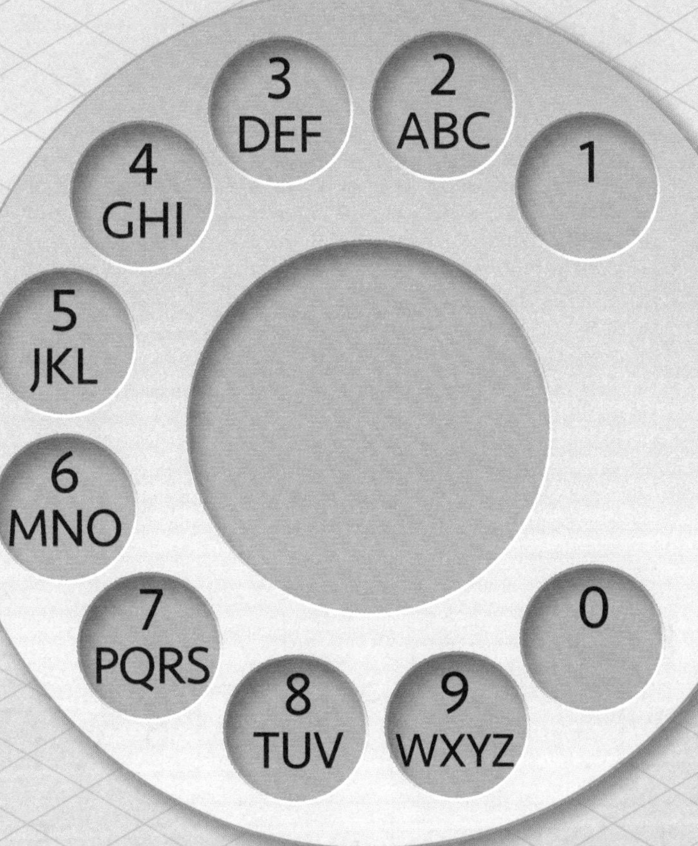

326435723254333
62825437678626
268664622633727
2723539266737
4255323779
5623279268

Answer see page 132

Assemble the pieces shown below into a square grid which reads the same across as it does downwards.

2	8
9	7

5	9	5

7	8
6	6

2	6
	4
	9

1
5
3
0

1	7	6
		6

9	5	4	6
	6		

5
4
6
1

	9
3	0
	5

	7	
7	3	9

7	6	4
	5	
	2	

2	9	2	8

09

Fill in the missing plus, minus, multiplication, division, and/or factorial signs to make the equation below correct, performing all calculations strictly in the order they appear on the page.

3 14 22 11 3 24 17 = 24

Answer see page 132

10

In each square, the arrow shows the direction you must move in. The numbers in some squares show that square's position in the correct sequence of moves. Move from top left to bottom right, visiting each square in the grid exactly once.

1 →	↓	↓	↓
4 ↓	↓	↘	←
↗	↑	←	↙
→	←	↑	16 ○

Answer see page 132

Answer see page 132

11

James likes iris but not peony. Nicole likes rose but not aster. Heather likes sunflower but not lily. Which of the following does Steven like?

LILAC HYDRANGEA

CARNATION TULIP

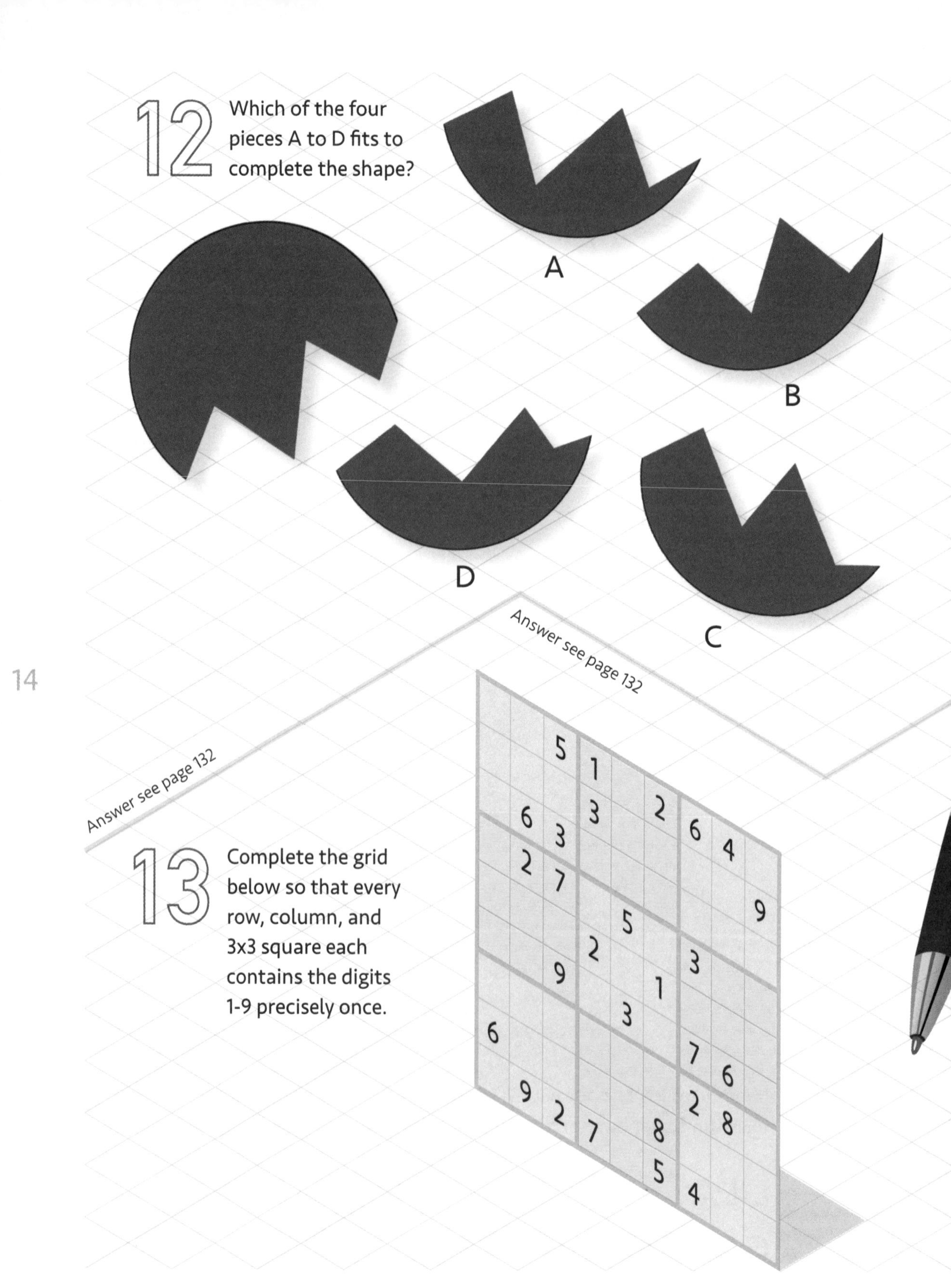

12

Which of the four pieces A to D fits to complete the shape?

Answer see page 132

13

Complete the grid below so that every row, column, and 3x3 square each contains the digits 1-9 precisely once.

Answer see page 132

14

Connect each pair of identical numbers with a single continuous path running horizontally and/or vertically through the cells of the grid below. Paths may switch direction at the centre of a cell, but may not branch, loop back on themselves, or cross. When the grid is complete, each cell will contain a single path section.

10	13	12	5						5
									11
				6	3			3	9
			11					6	
			9						
		8				2	7	4	
		1							
				1		2			
		10		13	8	7		4	12

Answer see page 132

15

Are the following statements true or false?

i. The blue-ringed octopus is one of only two octopus species deadly to mankind.
ii. Playing cards were invented around 1200 years ago in China.
iii. Arcturus is the brightest star in the constellation of Boötes.
iv. Helium is the most common substance in the universe.
v. Antwerp is a city in Belgium.
vi. Pansies used to be known as “Love in Idleness”.
vii. Jan Tyssowski was a former dictator of Yugoslavia.
viii. Swords were invented in South America more than 3000 years ago.
ix. 1000 is a square number.
x. Phoenix is the capital of Arizona.

Answer see page 132

The grid below shows the numbers on a full set of dominoes, from 0-0 to 9-9 inclusive, that have been pushed together horizontally and vertically to make a solid rectangle. Complete the grid to show where each domino lies.

2	4	9	5	5	0	6	7	6	6	9
7	5	1	2	7	3	3	0	8	8	9
4	4	9	1	4	4	1	2	4	2	3
5	9	8	9	6	5	4	3	5	3	8
5	0	1	1	4	0	4	0	2	7	8
0	7	5	9	2	2	6	4	6	2	1
9	7	1	7	7	5	5	9	0	2	6
6	5	8	3	0	2	0	0	3	7	3
9	2	3	3	8	8	7	6	0	1	1
6	8	9	1	8	8	3	6	7	1	4

Answer see page 132

Answer see page 132

17

The pieces can be assembled into a regular geometric shape. What is it?

Shade the cells in the grid below so that each row and column holds continuous lines of shaded cells of the lengths indicated by the numbers shown at the start of that row or column. Blocks are separated from others in the same row or column by at least one empty cell. A picture will emerge when the cells are shaded correctly.

Column clues (left to right):

1	2	3	4	5	6	7	8	9	10	11	12	13	14	15	16	17	18	19	20	21	22	23
			2				1	1												3		
4	7	2	8	2	1	1	8	7	1						8				6	3		
2	5	12	1	7	10	11	2	1	7	7	7	10	11	11	1	9	14	14	3	1	6	3

Row clues (top to bottom):

7
4
3, 1, 1
2, 2, 2
2, 5
3, 4, 2
22
22
20
18
17
17
18
3, 3, 7
3, 2, 3, 3
3, 3, 3, 3
3, 3, 3, 3

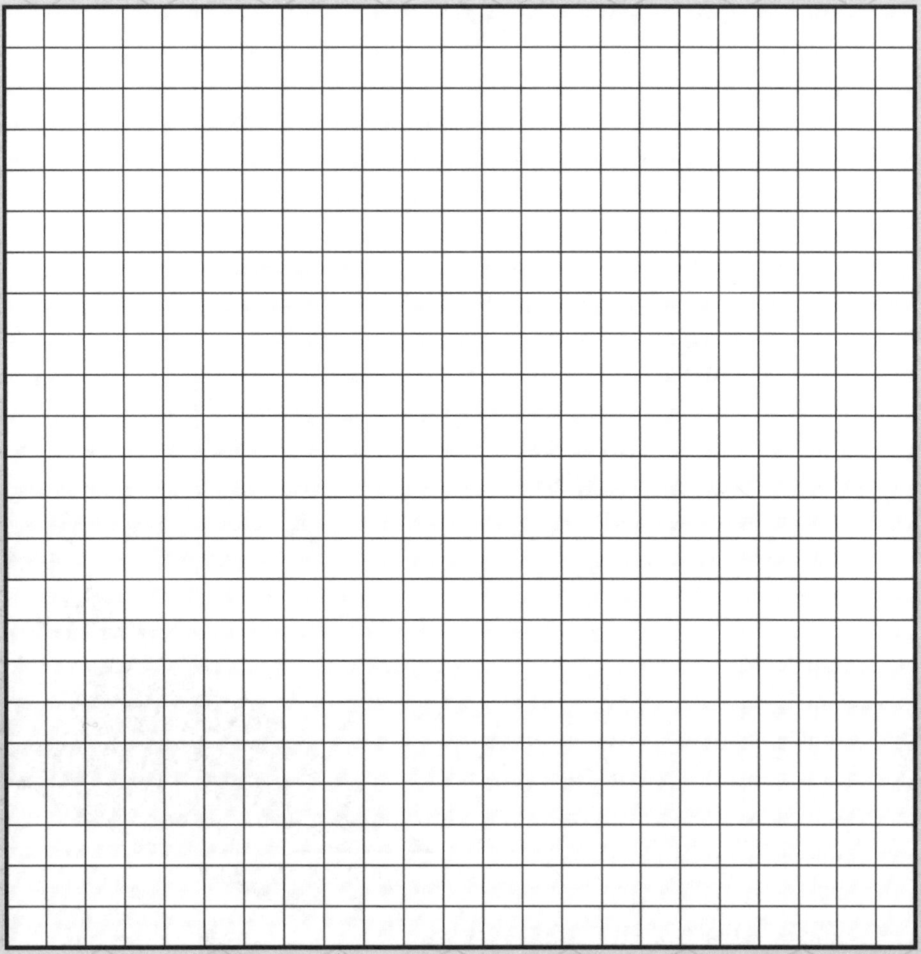

Answer see page 132

Ten vessels are hidden in the grid below, four one cell ships, three two-cell ships, two three-cell ships, and one four-cell ship. Ships are positioned horizontally or vertically. No two ships are immediately adjacent to each other, including diagonally. The numbers next to each row and column show the total number of ship segments in that line. Identify the exact locations of all ten vessels. Some ship segments and/or spaces of empty ocean are shown to assist you.

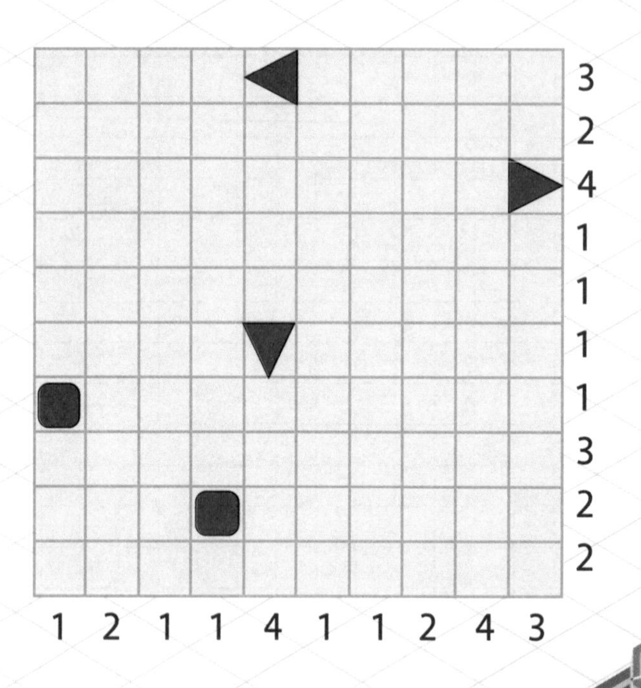

Answer see page 132

Complete the grid below so that every row and column each contains the digits 1-6 precisely once. A cell with a chevron pointing into it is smaller than the cell on the other side of the chevron.

21

What number should replace the question mark?

Answer see page 133

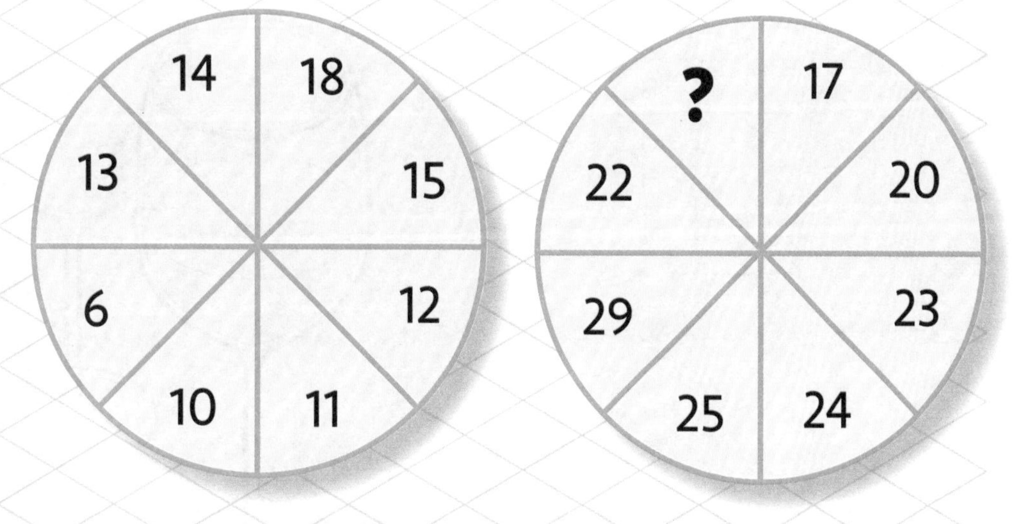

22

From the information below, what is the name of the merchant who likes Bordeaux?

The merchant from Paris liked wines from Alsace, but was not the blacksmith, who was named Georges. Michel, a goldsmith, was not a fan of Alsace wine. The merchant from Reims enjoyed Bordeaux wine. One of the merchants preferred to drink Burgundy. The whitesmith from Rouen was neither Jacques nor Veronique. The merchant who preferred Champagne was not named Iva or Michel. Jacques liked Beaujolais, and was not a tinsmith. The merchant from Bagnol was not a greensmith. One of the merchants was from Aix.

2 3 4

1

4

3

Answer see page 133

23

Using six straight lines, which must each touch at least one edge of the box, divide the design below into seven sections, each containing precisely nine circles.

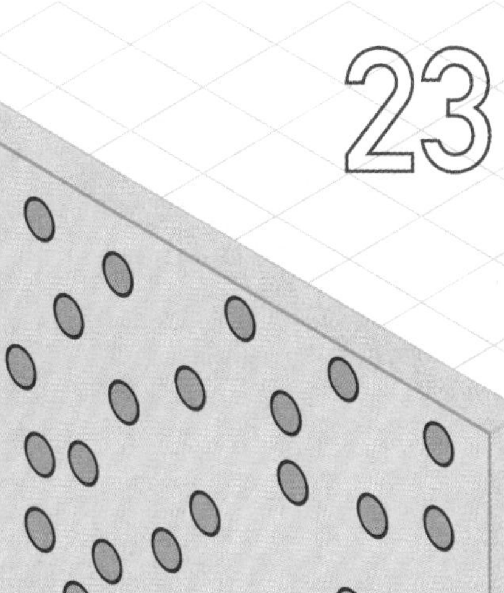

Answer see page 133

Answer see page 133

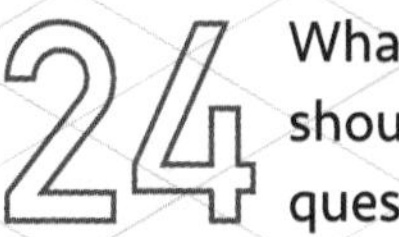

24

What number should replace the question mark?

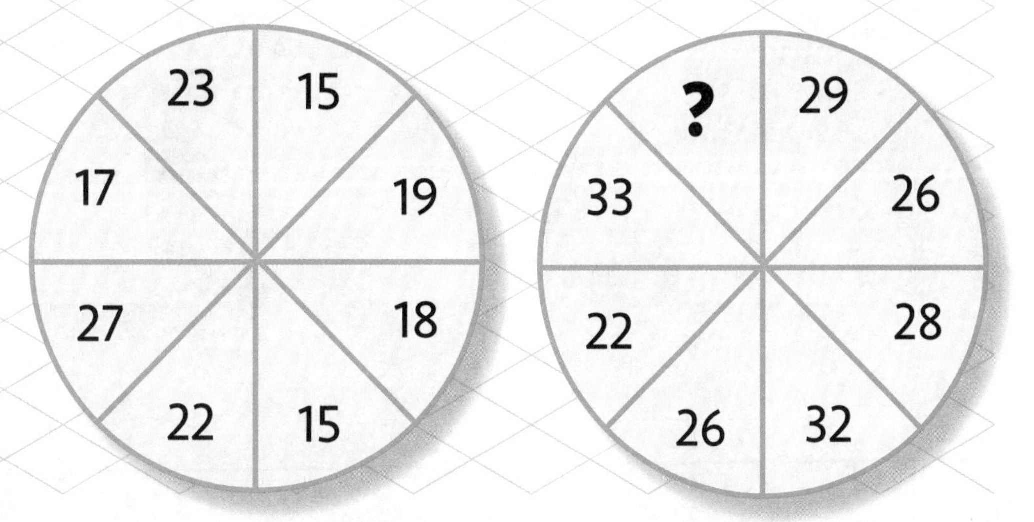

Complete the grid below so that each unbroken horizontal and vertical stretch of light cells sums to the total indicated in the cell to the left or above the stretch respectively. Each cell may contain only the digits 1 – 9, and no digit may be repeated in any given stretch of cells.

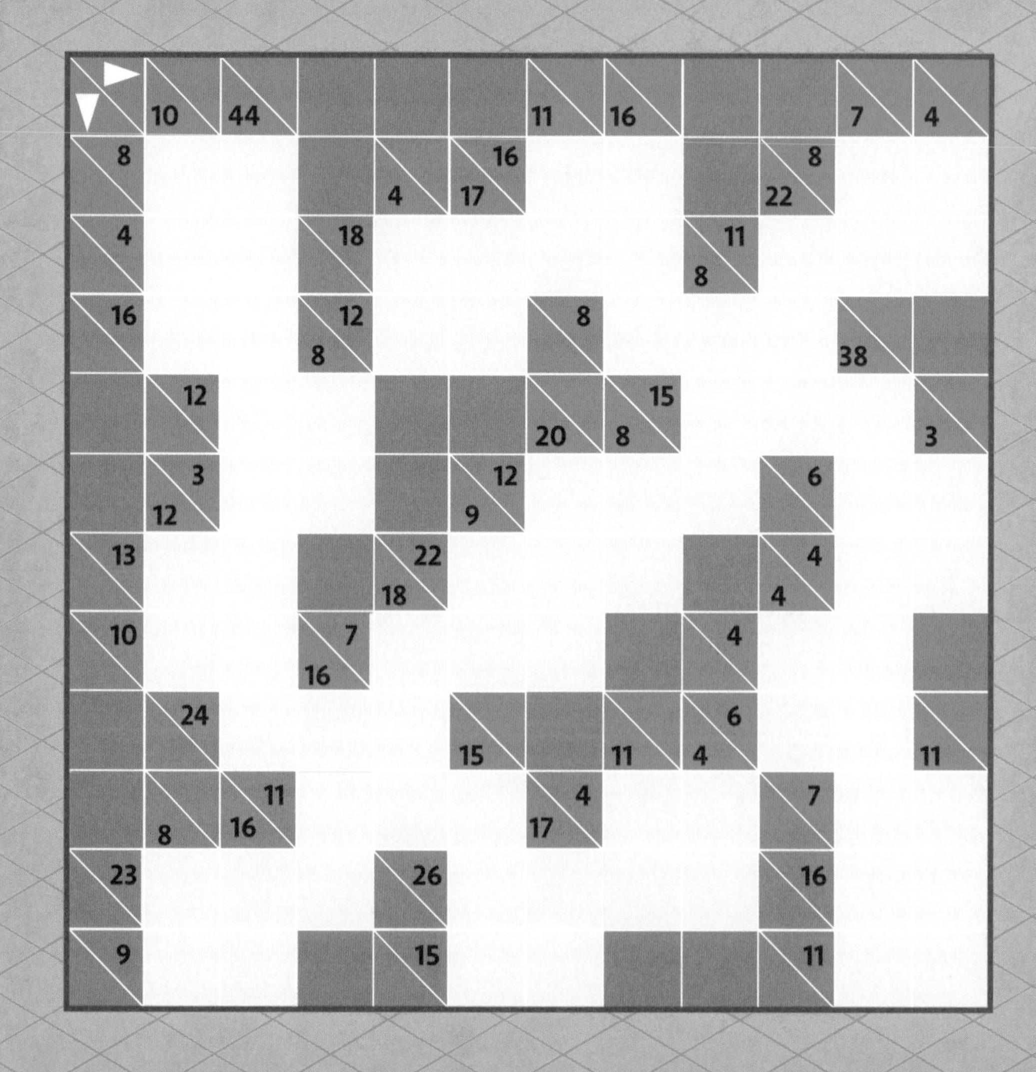

Answer see page 133

26

Which of the four pieces A to D fits to complete the shape?

A

B

C

D

Answer see page 133

Answer see page 133

27

What number should replace the question mark?

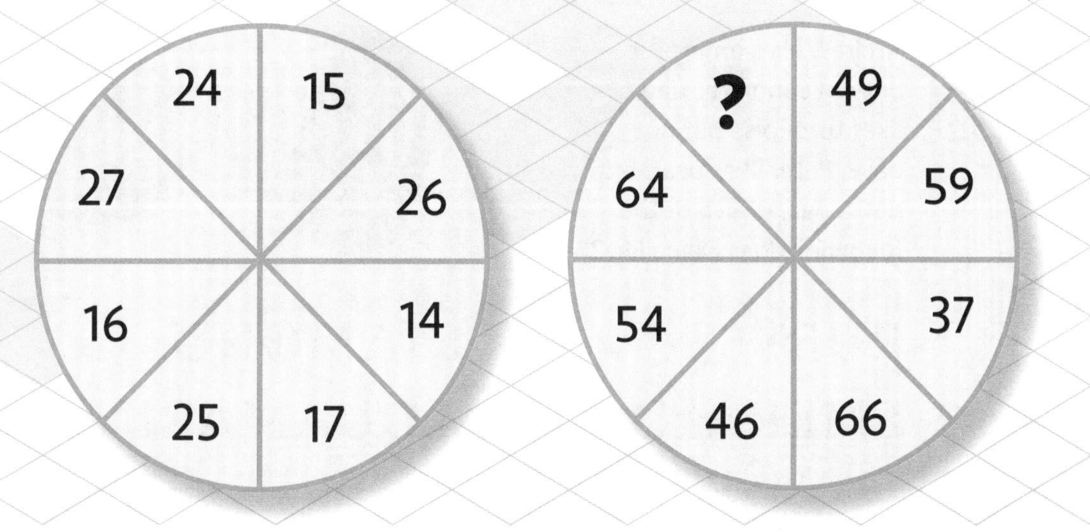

28

Which two cubes show three identical faces to each other?

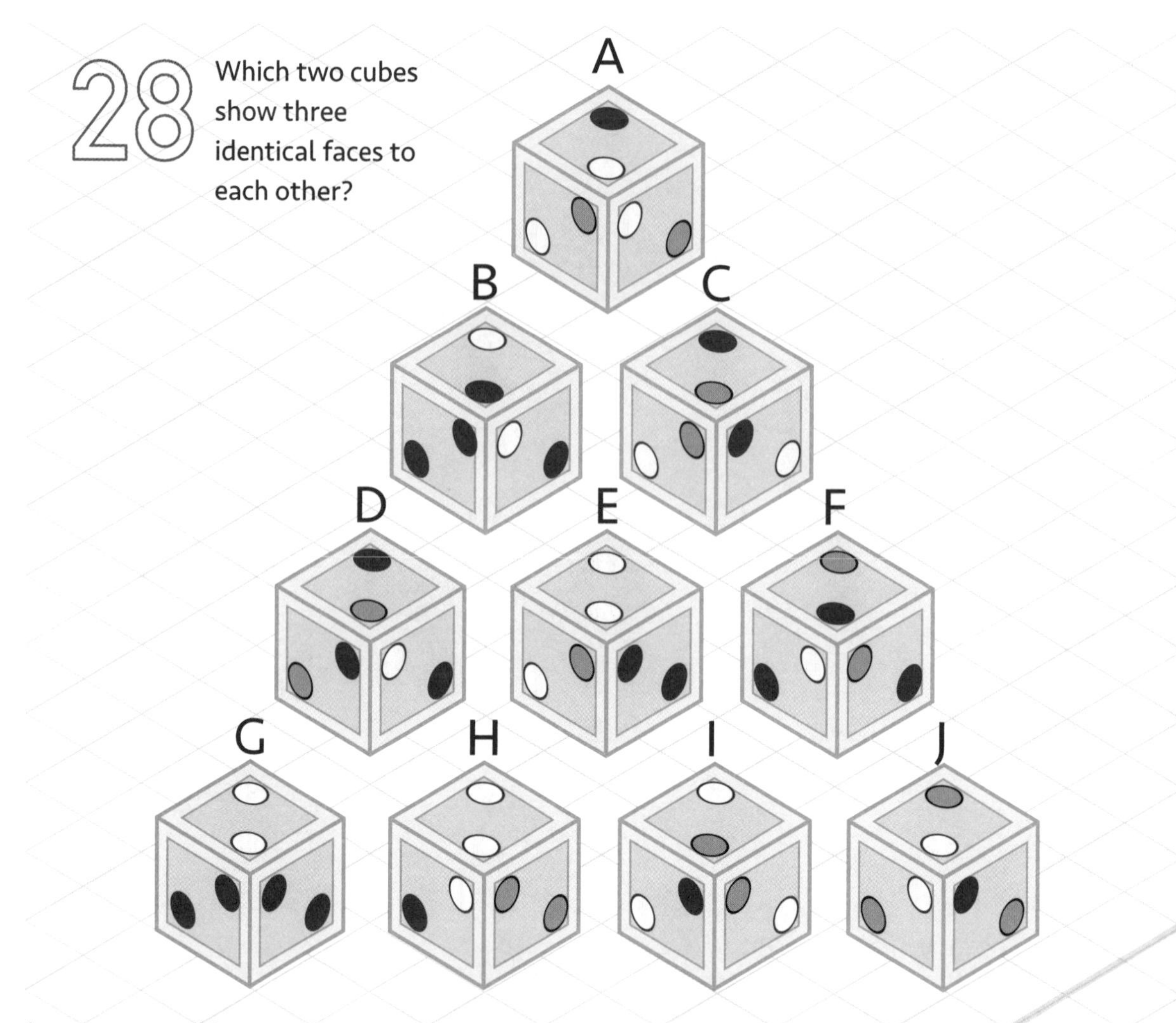

Answer see page 133

Answer see page 133

29

Andrew likes amethyst but not sapphire. Tina likes turquoise but not onyx. Peter likes pearl but not topaz. Which of the following does Diana like?

RUBY

DIAMOND

EMERALD

AQUAMARINE

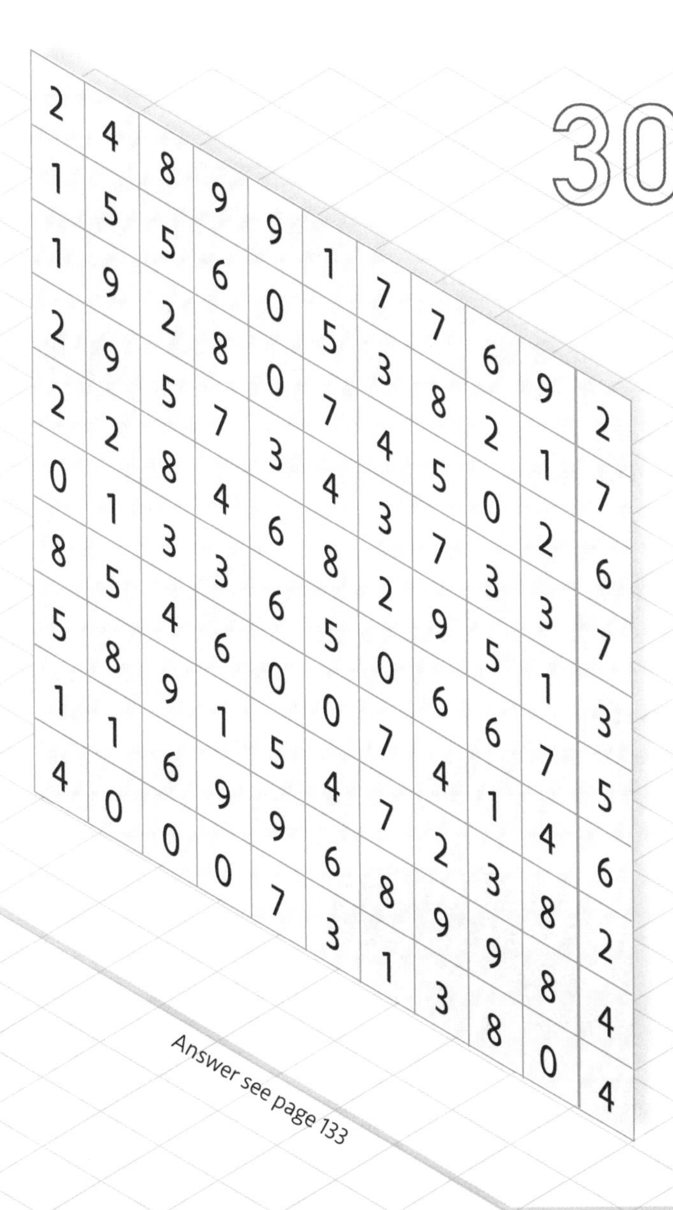

2	4	8	9	9	1	7	7	6	9	2
1	5	5	6	0	5	3	8	2	1	7
1	9	2	8	0	7	4	5	0	2	6
2	9	5	7	3	4	3	7	3	3	7
2	2	8	4	6	8	2	9	5	1	3
0	1	3	3	6	5	0	6	6	7	5
8	5	4	6	0	0	7	4	1	4	6
5	8	9	1	5	4	7	2	3	8	2
1	1	6	9	9	6	8	9	9	8	4
4	0	0	0	7	3	1	3	8	0	4

30

The grid below shows the numbers on a full set of dominoes, from 0-0 to 9-9 inclusive, that have been pushed together horizontally and vertically to make a solid rectangle. Complete the grid to show where each domino lies.

Answer see page 133

Answer see page 133

31

Fill in the missing plus, minus, multiplication, division, and/or factorial signs to make the equation below correct, performing all calculations strictly in the order they appear on the page.

17 25 19 15 4 23 8 = 72

Connect each pair of identical numbers with a single continuous path running horizontally and/or vertically through the cells of the grid below. Paths may switch direction at the centre of a cell, but may not branch, loop back on themselves, or cross. When the grid is complete, each cell will contain a single path section.

7	4		4	11					12
	9					6	11	3	5
	8	10							
					12	6			
			2			2			
						10			
7	8	1				1	9	3	5

Answer see page 133

Answer see page 133

Which of the four pieces A to D fits to complete the shape?

A

B

C

D

Tracey likes aquamarine but not beige. Jeffrey likes firebrick but not gold. Susan likes sienna but not khaki. Which of the following does William like?

PURPLE

IVORY

LAVENDER

OLIVE

Complete the grid below so that each unbroken horizontal and vertical stretch of light cells sums to the total indicated in the cell to the left or above the stretch respectively. Each cell may contain only the digits 1 – 9, and no digit may be repeated in any given stretch of cells.

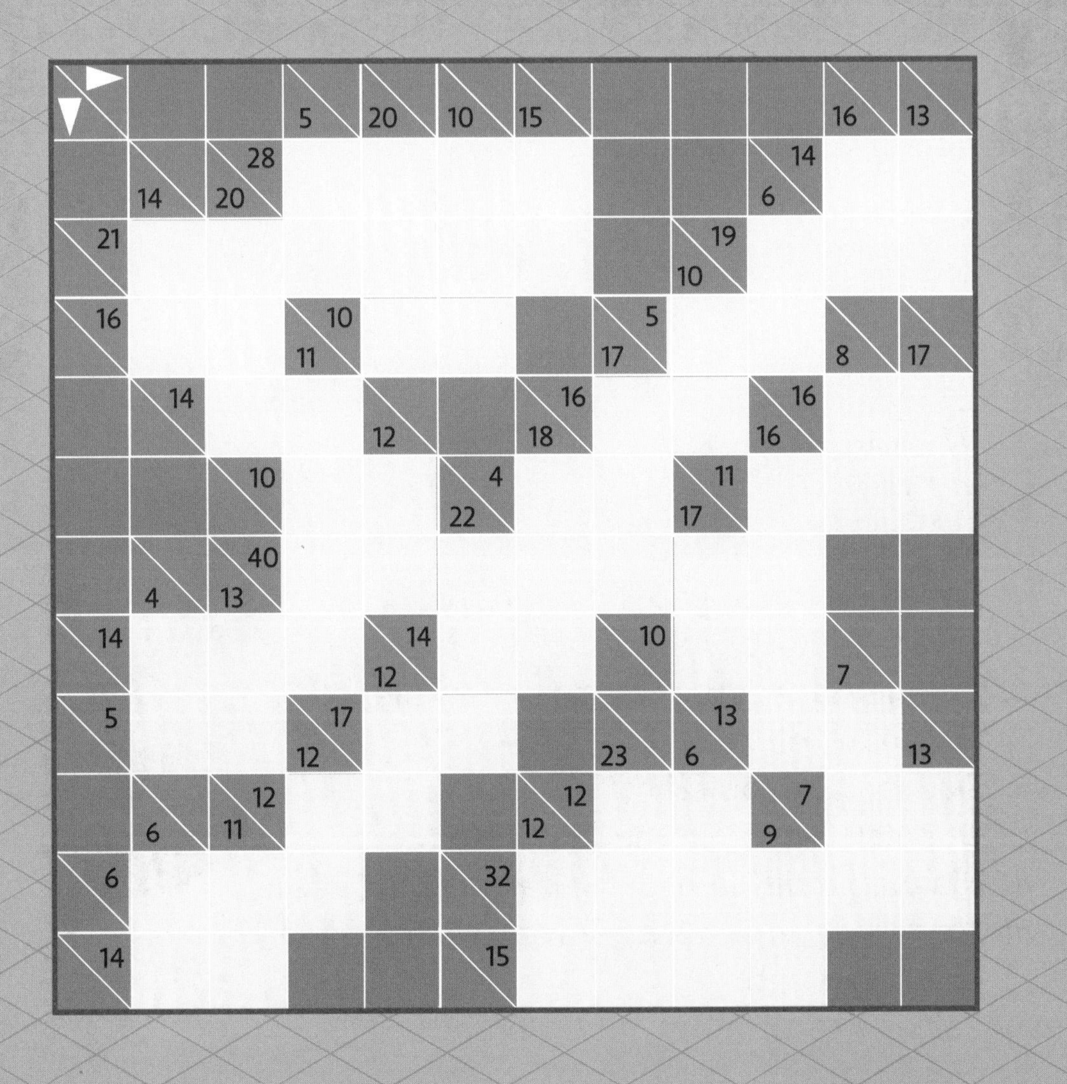

Answer see page 133

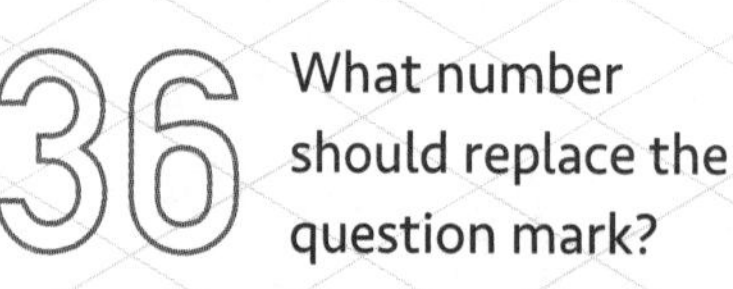

36

What number should replace the question mark?

8 4 10 7 5

7 5 9 6 3

2 6 4 8 4

9 5 ? 4 5

Answer see page 133

37

Are the following statements true or false?

i. 46 is a hexagonal number.
ii. Capella is the brightest star in the constellation of Auriga.
iii. Colonel Saye Zerbo was a former ruler of Oman.
iv. Dallas is the capital of Texas.
v. Donetsk is a city in the Ukraine.
vi. Magnesium is named after an area in Greece.
vii. Negative numbers were invented in Arabia 1200 years ago.
viii. Solo is a card game for four players.
ix. The floral genus Aquilegia is better known as the foxgloves.
x. There are five species of mammal that lay eggs.

Answer see page 133

Decipher the names of several celebrities using the telephone dial as a guide.

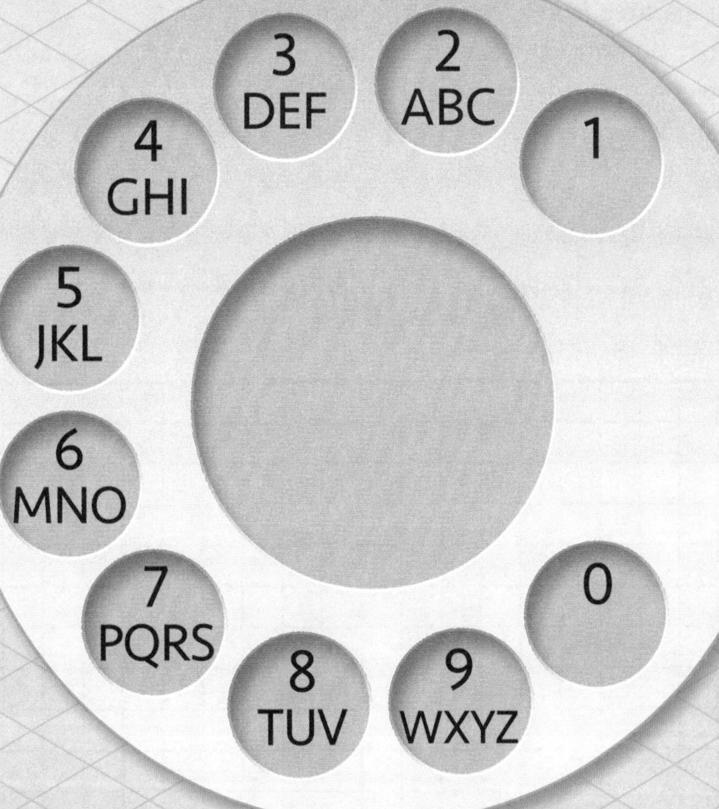

25722466

52534955364225

94553377355

63426369

72683555225766

86642657

Answer see page 134

Shade the cells in the grid below so that each row and column holds continuous lines of shaded cells of the lengths indicated by the numbers shown at the start of that row or column. Blocks are separated from others in the same row or column by at least one empty cell. A picture will emerge when the cells are shaded correctly.

Answer see page 134

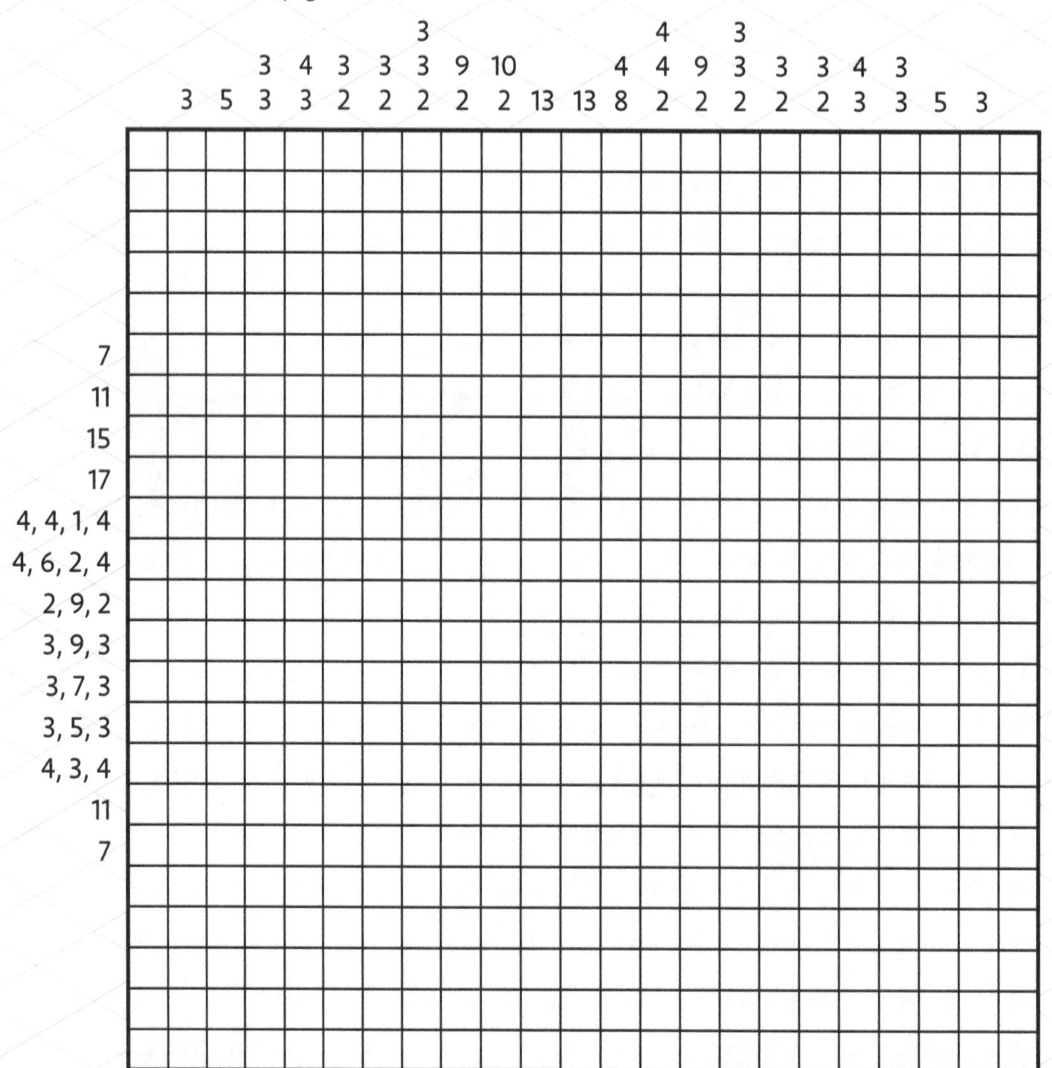

40

Ten vessels are hidden in the grid below, four one cell ships, three two-cell ships, two three-cell ship, and one four-cell ships. Ships are positioned horizontally or vertically. No two ships are immediately adjacent to each other, including diagonally. The numbers next to each row and column show the total number of ship segments in that line. Identify the exact locations of all ten vessels. Some ship segments and/or spaces of empty ocean are shown to assist you.

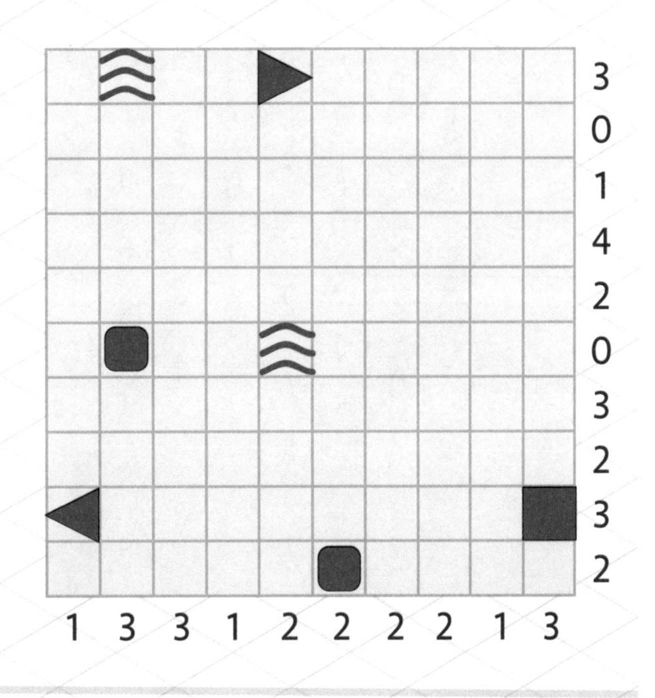

Answer see page 134

Answer see page 134

41

The pieces can be assembled into a regular geometric shape. What is it?

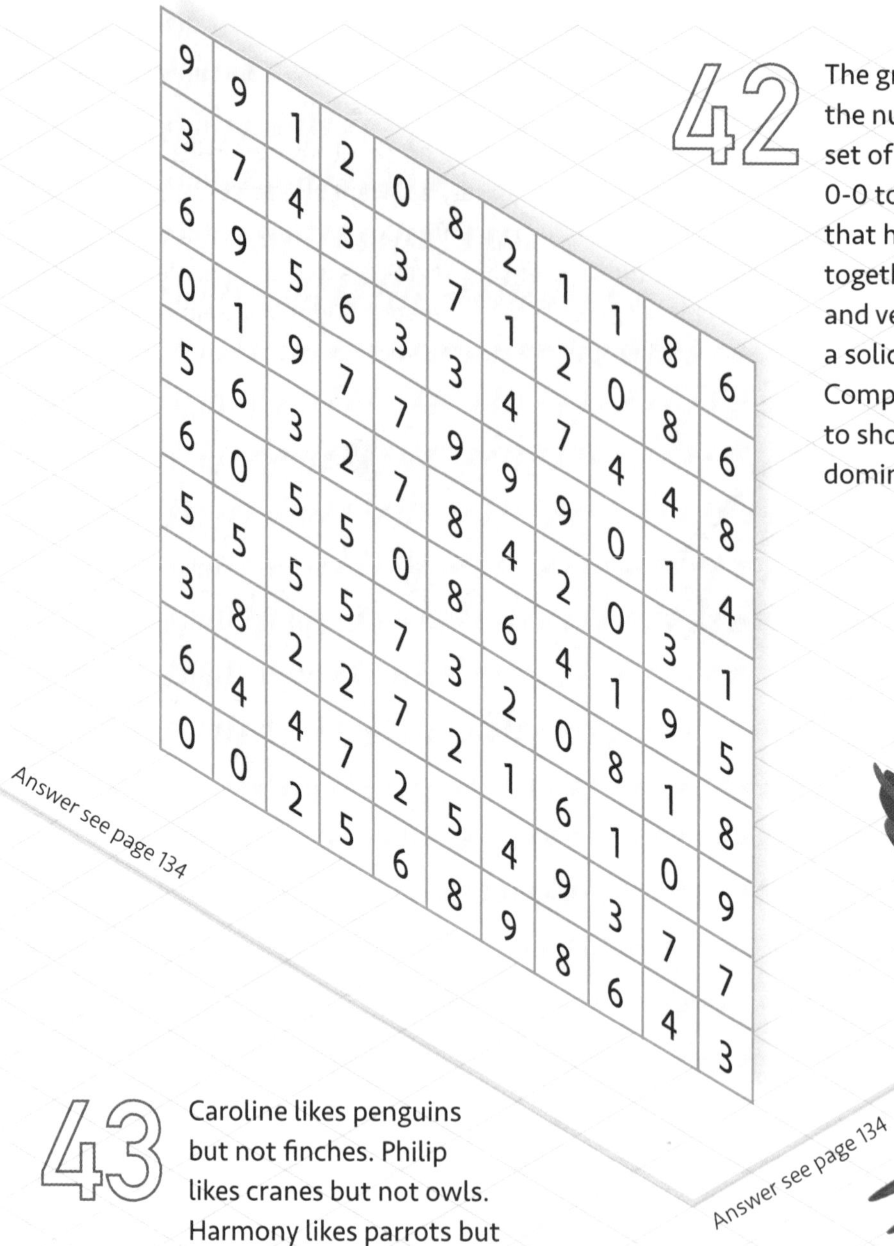

9	9	1	2	0	8	2	1	1	8	6
3	7	4	3	3	7	1	2	0	8	6
6	9	5	6	3	3	4	7	4	4	8
0	1	9	7	7	9	9	9	0	1	4
5	6	3	2	7	8	4	2	0	3	1
6	0	5	5	0	8	6	4	1	9	5
5	5	5	5	7	3	2	0	8	1	8
3	8	2	2	7	2	1	6	1	0	9
6	4	4	7	2	5	4	9	3	7	7
0	0	2	5	6	8	9	8	6	4	3

Answer see page 134

42

The grid below shows the numbers on a full set of dominoes, from 0-0 to 9-9 inclusive, that have been pushed together horizontally and vertically to make a solid rectangle. Complete the grid to show where each domino lies.

Answer see page 134

43

Caroline likes penguins but not finches. Philip likes cranes but not owls. Harmony likes parrots but not hummingbirds. Which of the following does Mellissa like?

SWALLOWS

SWIFTS

CUCKOOS

WOODPECKERS

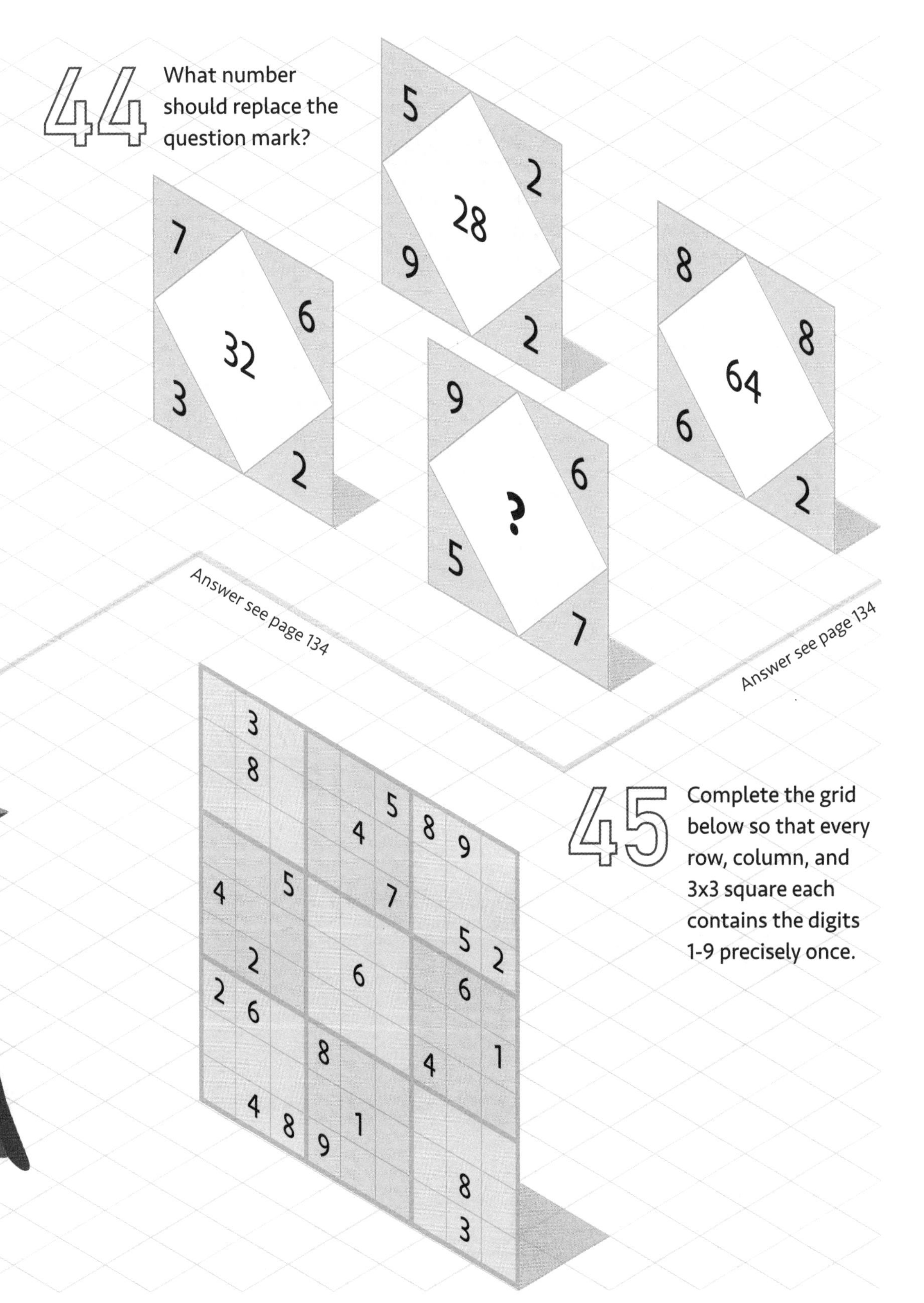

44

What number should replace the question mark?

Answer see page 134

45

Complete the grid below so that every row, column, and 3x3 square each contains the digits 1-9 precisely once.

Answer see page 134

Complete the grid below so that every row, column, and 3x3 square each contains the digits 1-9 precisely once. The sum of the digits in each group of cells with a dotted outline must total the number in the group's top left corner.

Answer see page 134

12	11		6		12		11	
	9	9		18	12		8	
9		13				14		17
			11			14		
12	6		16	4	14		8	
	17					3		11
7		14	10		25	7		
17			9			10		21
		8						

Answer see page 134

47

In the grid below, how much is each symbol worth?

12

18

10

13

16

Complete the grid below so that each unbroken horizontal and vertical stretch of light cells sums to the total indicated in the cell to the left or above the stretch respectively. Each cell may contain only the digits 1 – 9, and no digit may be repeated in any given stretch of cells.

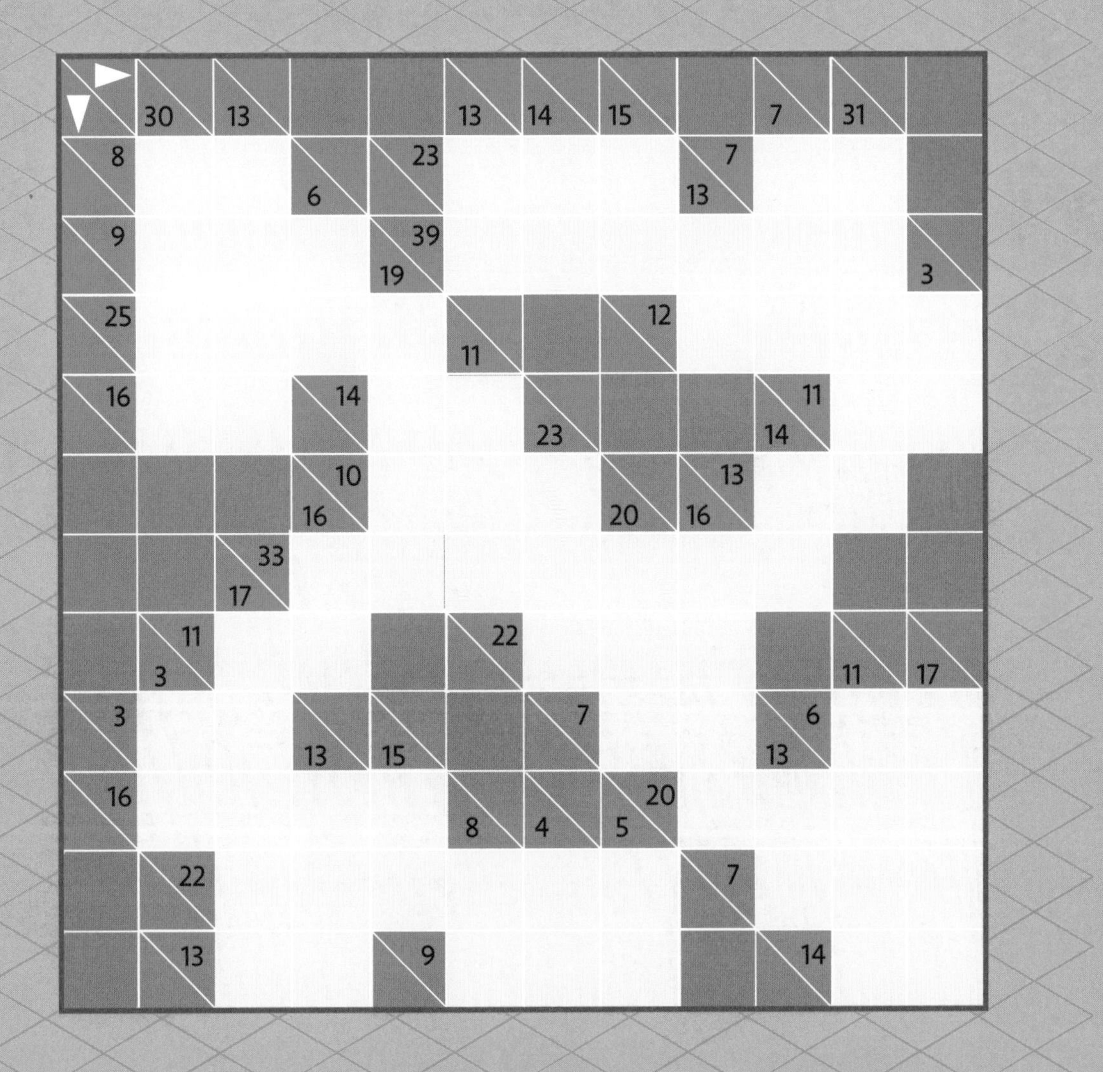

Answer see page 134

Decipher the names of several celebrities using the telephone dial as a guide.

3 DEF
2 ABC
1
4 GHI
5 JKL
6 MNO
7 PQRS
8 TUV
9 WXYZ
0

7437232767626
62228529285546
675263625666
53472564448539
366278663
787735527693

Answer see page 134

50

Using four straight lines, divide the design below into seven sections, each containing precisely eight circles.

Answer see page 134

51

Are the following statements true or false?

Answer see page 134

i. Deneb is the brightest star in the constellation of Crux.
ii. Jorge Montt was a former ruler of Algeria.
iii. Match-sticks were invented in China 1400 years ago.
iv. Minsk is a city in Lithuania.
v. Promethium is the only element with no stable isotope.
vi. Providence is the capital of Rhode Island.
vii. Rummy is a trick-taking card game.
viii. The Aztec people called armadillos 'Turtle-Rabbits'.
ix. The English daisy, Bellis perennis, does not close up at night.
x. The numbers (20, 99, 101) form a Pythagorean triple.

52

From the information below, what was the favourite food of the person who was born in California?

The person who said tofu was their favourite food was a teacher, and was not the auburn-haired person, who was born in Wales. The person from Cyprus loved cherries, and was neither blonde nor grey-haired. One of the group was a therapist, and another had fresh bread as their favourite food. The person who loved lamb was a counsellor. The nurse was neither bald nor black-haired. The person who was born in Provence did not love chocolate. The bald person, who was born in Tuscany, was not a teacher. The blonde person was a trainer, and was not born in California.

2 3 4

1

4

3

Answer see page 134

Simon Barker likes Everest but not Denali. Debi Jenkins likes Kilimanjaro but not Elbrus. Anthony Richardson likes Damavand but not Mont Blanc. Which of the following does Tristan Kennedy like?

SEREBUS

KANGCHENJUNGA

TEIDE

YUSHAN

Answer see page 134

Answer see page 134

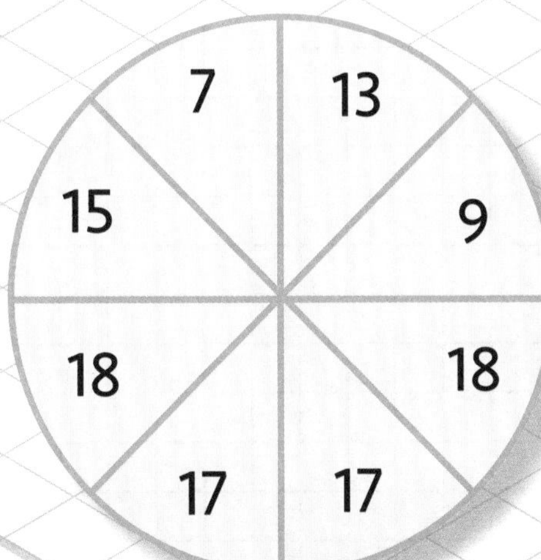

54 What number should replace the question mark?

Answer see page 135

In each square, the arrow shows the direction you must move in. The numbers in some squares show that square's position in the correct sequence of moves. Move from top left to bottom right, visiting each square in the grid exactly once.

Shade the cells in the grid below so that each row and column holds continuous lines of shaded cells of the lengths indicated by the numbers shown at the start of that row or column. Blocks are separated from others in the same row or column by at least one empty cell. A picture will emerge when the cells are shaded correctly.

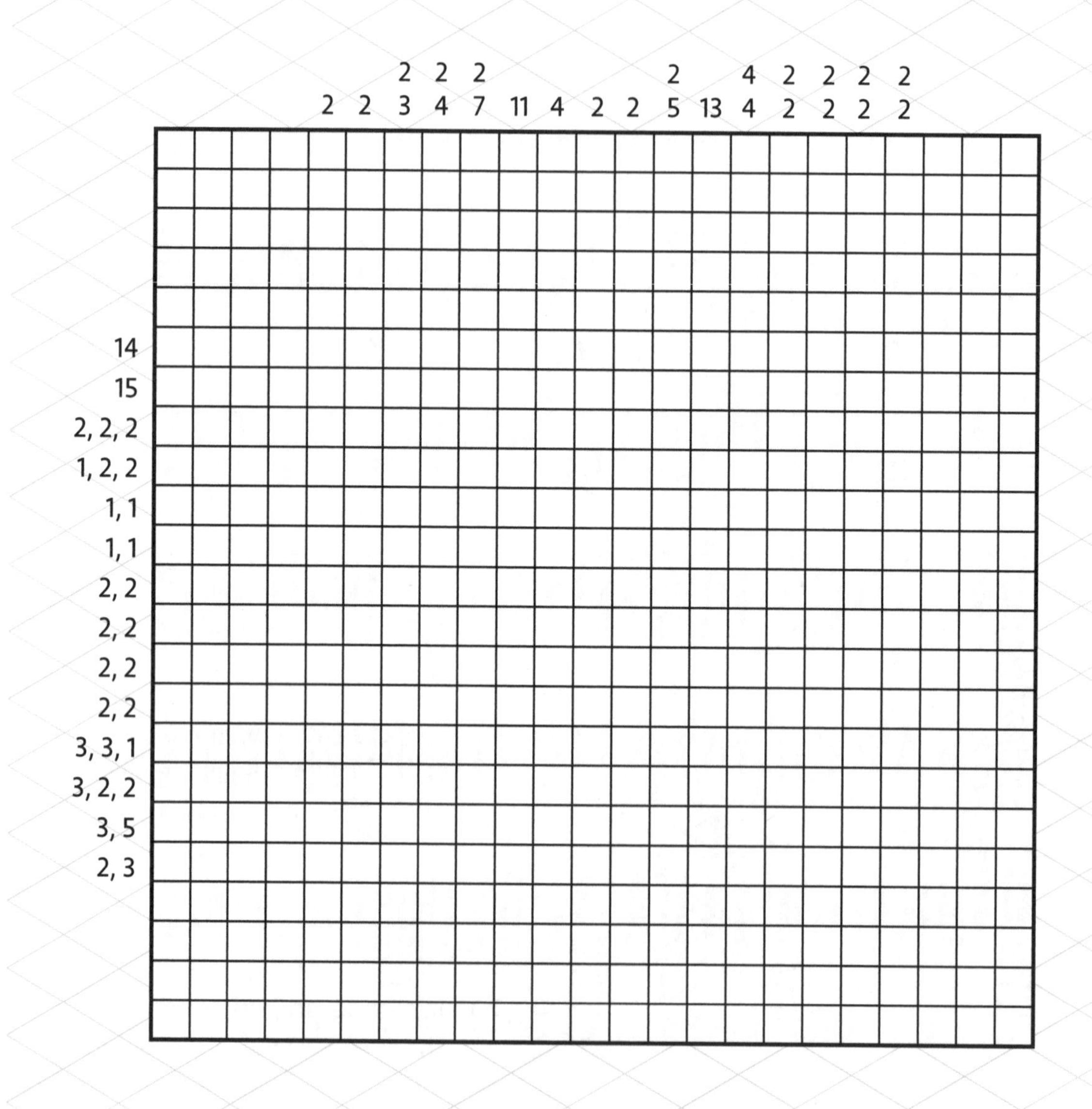

Answer see page 135

Which symbols are missing from the grid below?

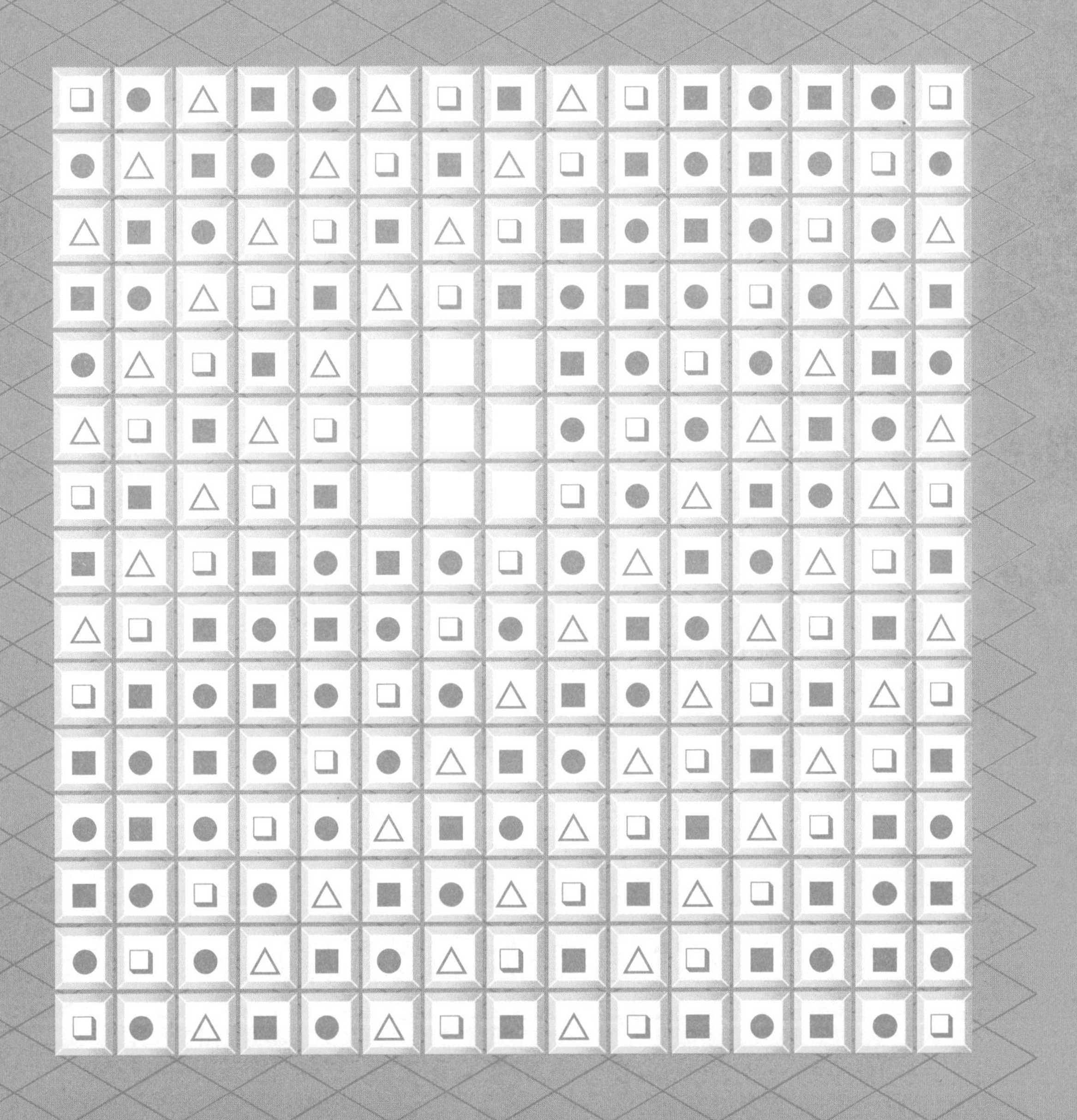

Answer see page 135

Decipher the names of several celebrities using the telephone dial as a guide.

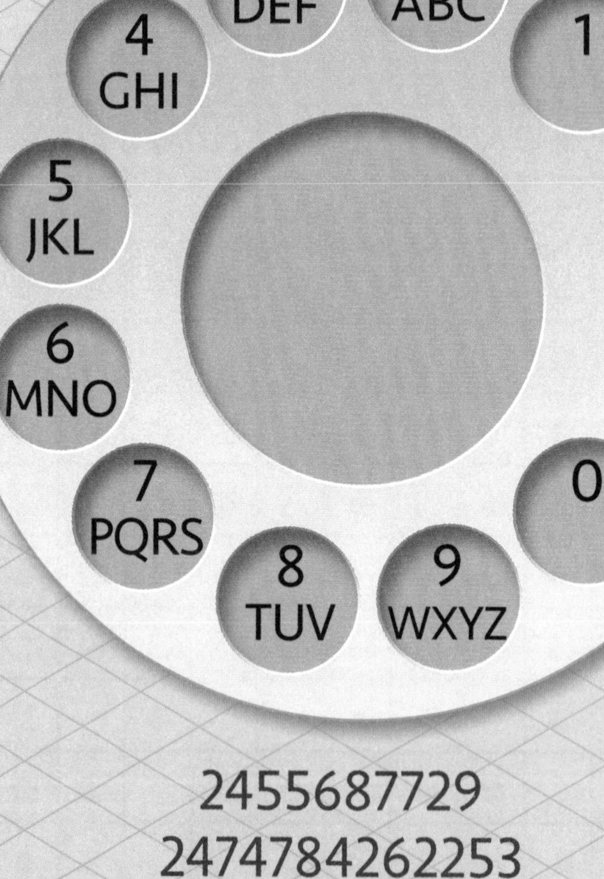

2455687729
2474784262253
42662535536
738377355377
64265272243
8664433537866

Answer see page 135

59

What number should replace the question mark?

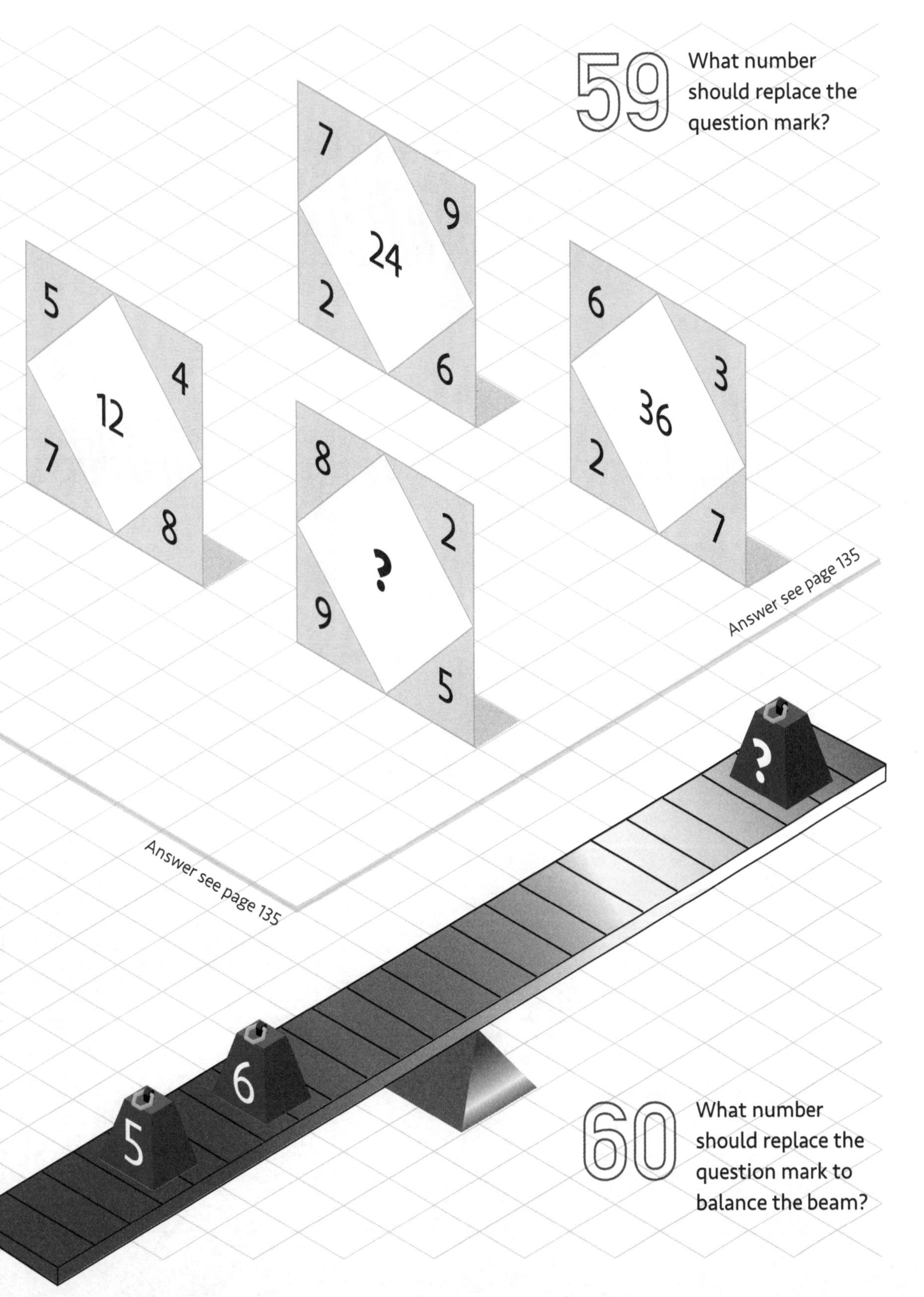

Answer see page 135

60

What number should replace the question mark to balance the beam?

Answer see page 135

Complete the grid below so that each unbroken horizontal and vertical stretch of light cells sums to the total indicated in the cell to the left or above the stretch respectively. Each cell may contain only the digits 1 – 9, and no digit may be repeated in any given stretch of cells.

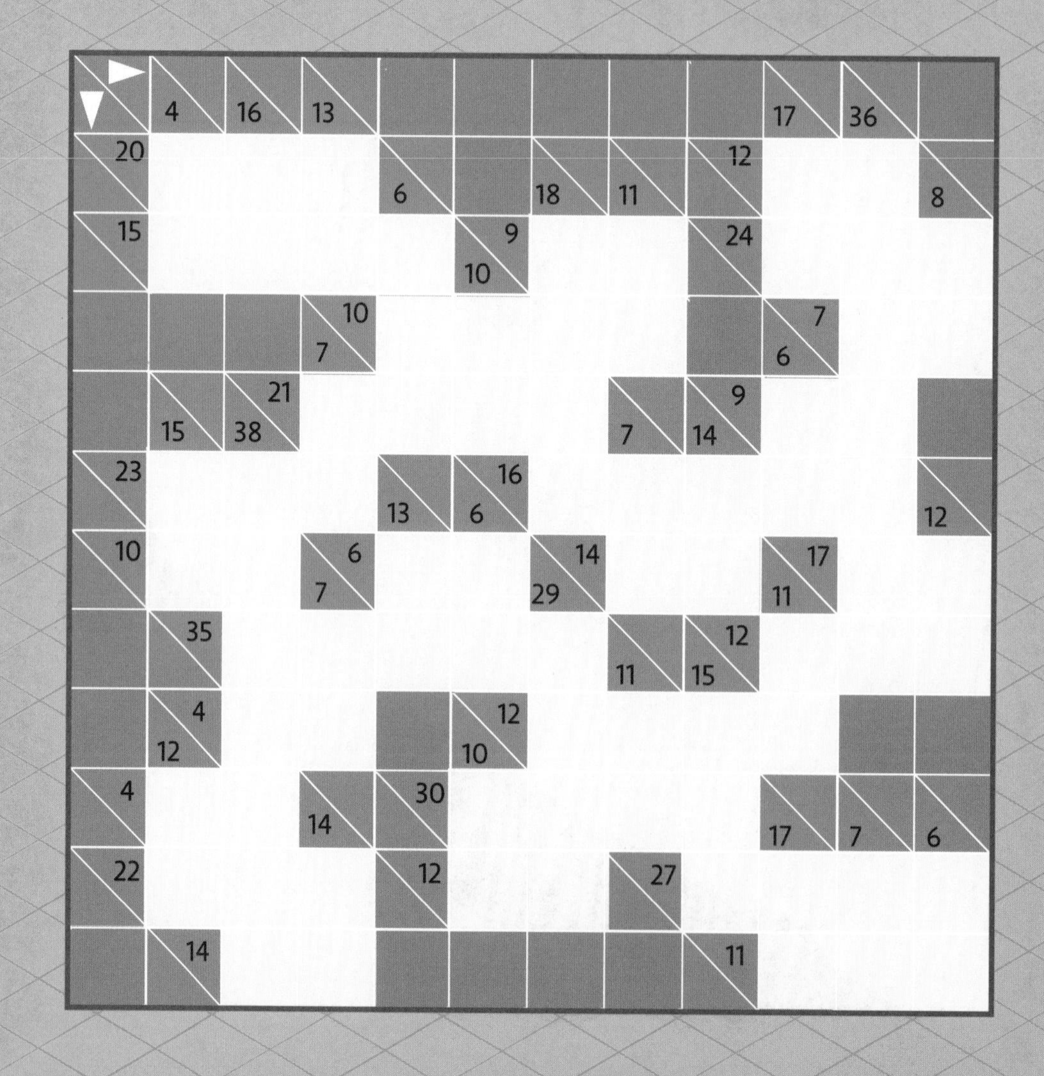

Answer see page 135

62

The grid below shows the numbers on a full set of dominoes, from 0-0 to 9-9 inclusive, that have been pushed together horizontally and vertically to make a solid rectangle. Complete the grid to show where each domino lies.

5	4	8	2	2	0	3	7	1	3	8
5	4	1	2	4	6	4	9	4	1	7
7	7	7	4	3	4	9	8	5	8	6
7	7	6	8	1	4	7	0	9	6	5
8	8	6	1	5	9	0	1	2	6	9
7	6	9	9	3	5	5	5	4	6	0
0	9	2	2	9	0	8	5	0	8	0
7	8	3	1	5	7	9	6	9	3	0
6	2	0	1	2	2	2	3	1	3	5
1	1	3	2	8	3	4	4	6	0	3

Answer see page 135

63

Which of the four objects A to D fits to complete the shape?

A

B

C

D

Answer see page 135

64

The grid below shows the numbers on a full set of dominoes, from 0-0 to 9-9 inclusive, that have been pushed together horizontally and vertically to make a solid rectangle. Complete the grid to show where each domino lies.

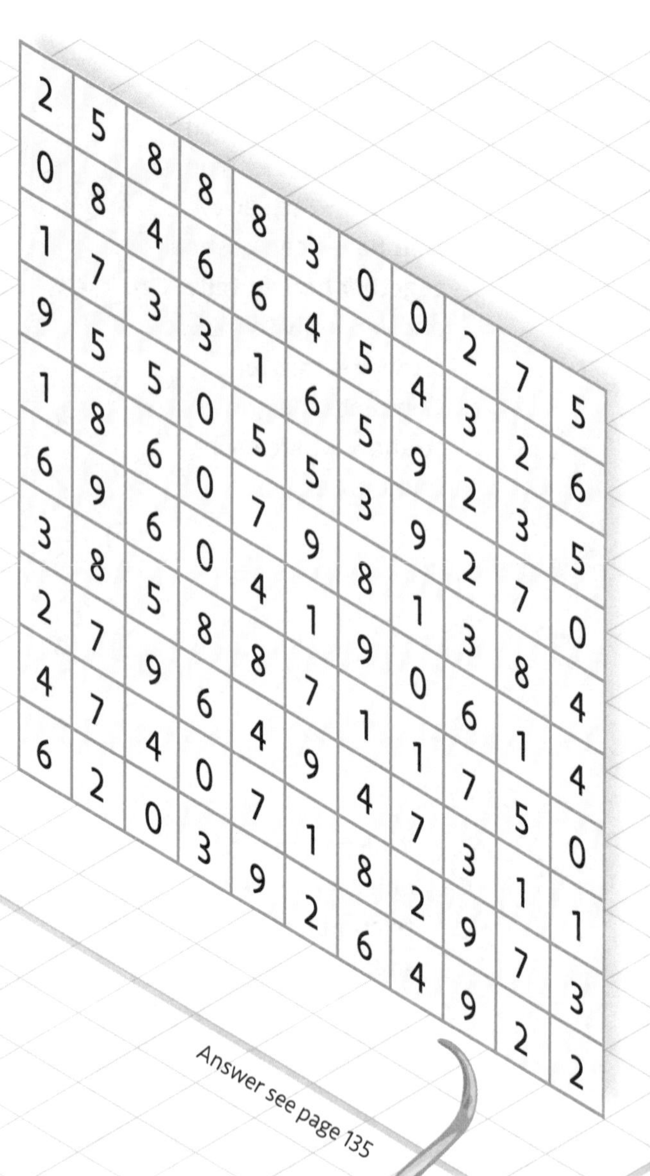

2	5	8	8	8	3	0	0	2	7	5
0	8	4	6	6	4	5	4	3	2	6
1	7	3	3	1	6	5	9	2	3	5
9	5	5	0	5	5	3	9	2	7	0
1	8	6	0	7	9	8	1	3	8	4
6	9	6	0	4	1	9	0	6	1	4
3	8	5	8	8	7	1	1	7	5	0
2	7	9	6	4	9	4	7	3	1	1
4	7	4	0	7	1	8	2	9	7	3
6	2	0	3	9	2	6	4	9	2	2

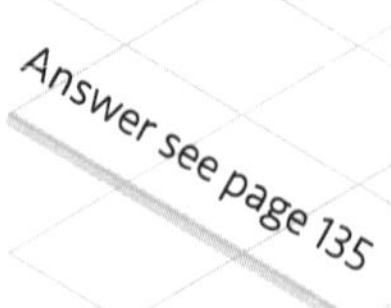
Answer see page 135

65

Complete the grid below so that every row and column each contains the digits 1-6 precisely once. A cell with a chevron pointing into it is smaller than the cell on the other side of the chevron.

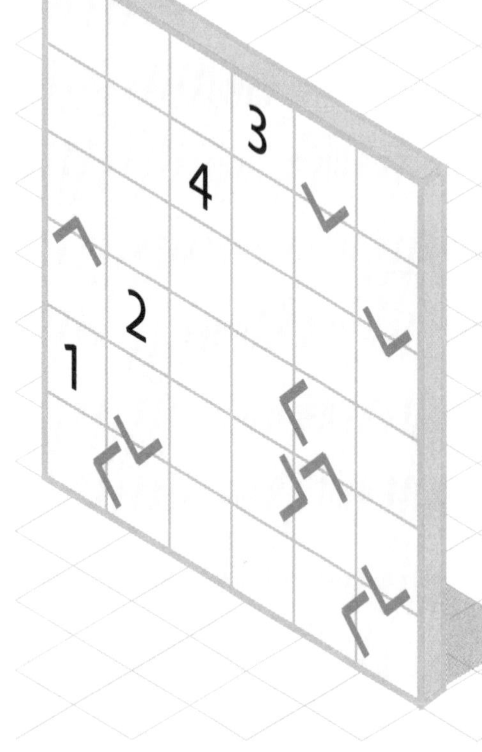

Answer see page 135

Complete the grid below so that every row, column, and 3x3 square each contains the digits 1-9 precisely once.

1		2			9			
				4		1		
7	3				8			
		4	7				5	
		9				6		
	6				2	9		
			8				3	9
		7		5				
			1			5		8

Answer see page 135

Answer see page 135

67

Are the following statements true or false?

i. 28 is a perfect number.
ii. Castor is the brightest star in the constellation of Gemini.
iii. Klondike is a card game for three players.
iv. Lithium is the lightest of all metals in the periodic table.
v. Madison is the capital of Wisconsin.
vi. Manuel Quezon was a former ruler of the Philippines.
vii. Native tulips can be found around the globe.
viii. The dinosaurs went completely extinct.
ix. The oldest existing university is in Morocco.
x. Wrexham is a town in England.

68

Ten vessels are hidden in the grid below, four one cell ships, three two-cell ships, two three-cell ships, and one four-cell ship. Ships are positioned horizontally or vertically. No two ships are immediately adjacent to each other, including diagonally. The numbers next to each row and column show the total number of ship segments in that line. Identify the exact locations of all ten vessels. Some ship segments and/or spaces of empty ocean are shown to assist you.

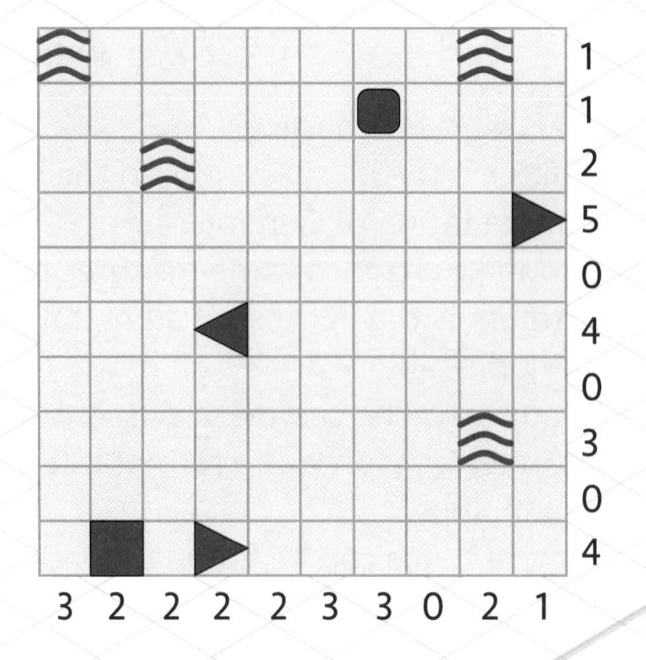

Answer see page 135

In the grid below, how much is each symbol worth?

28

21

23

25

25

27

Answer see page 135

Answer see page 135

7

?

70

What number should replace the question mark to balance the beam?

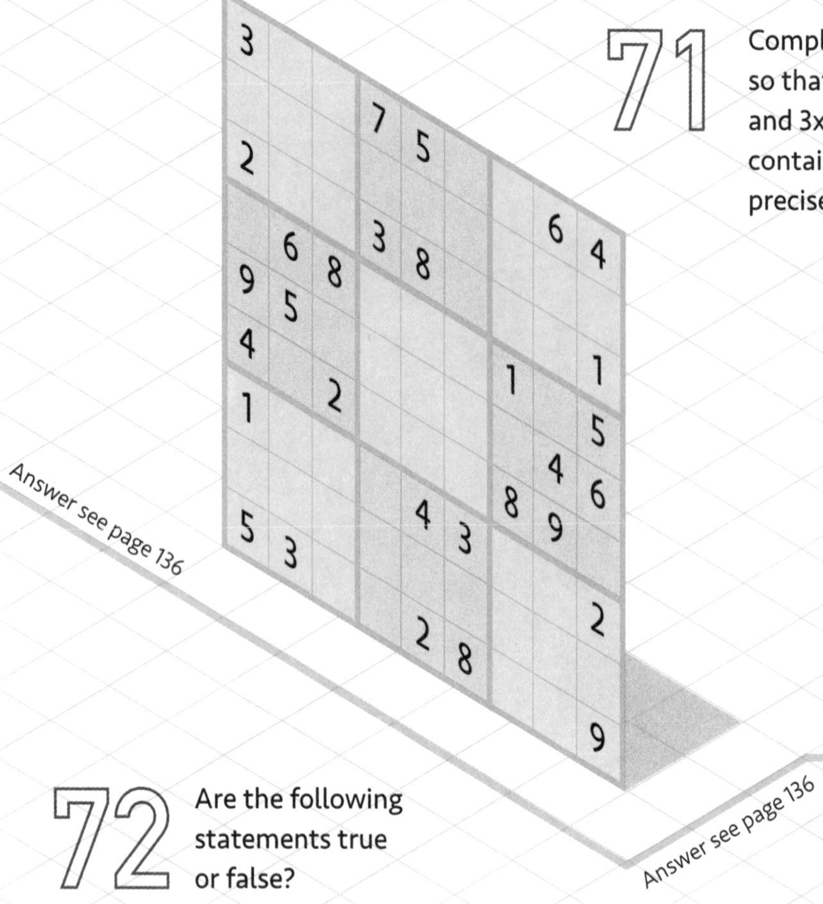

71

Complete the grid below so that every row, column, and 3x3 square each contains the digits 1-9 precisely once.

3			7	5			6	4
2			3	8				1
	6	8				1		5
9	5						4	6
4		2				8	9	
1				4	3			2
5	3			2	8			9

Answer see page 136

72

Are the following statements true or false?

i. 537 is a prime number.
ii. Fluorine will react with almost all other elements.
iii. Gunpowder was invented in India in the 9th century AD.
iv. Nabis was a former tyrant of Sicily.
v. New York City is the capital of New York state.
vi. Pazin is a city in Serbia.
vii. Rigel is the brightest star in the constellation of Orion.
viii. Senet was a board game played in ancient Egypt 5,000 years ago.
ix. Some parrots have been shown to understand, and correctly use, hundreds of words of human language.
x. The daffodil is part of the floral genus Narcissus.

Answer see page 136

73

Are the following statements true or false?

i. 78 is a triangular number.
ii. In a 52-card deck, there are ~10^25 possible orderings of the cards.
iii. Jerry Rawlings was a former ruler of Ghana.
iv. Kazan is a city in Estonia.
v. Los Angeles is the capital of California.
vi. Mirrors were invented 2500 years ago in the Lebanon.
vii. Silicon is a non-metallic element.
viii. Sirius is the brightest star in the constellation of Canis Minor.
ix. There are no wild alpacas we know of.
x. There is a type of rose named after British trade unionist Arthur Scargill.

Answer see page 136

74

In each square, the arrow shows the direction you must move in. The numbers in some squares show that square's position in the correct sequence of moves. Move from top left to bottom right, visiting each square in the grid exactly once.

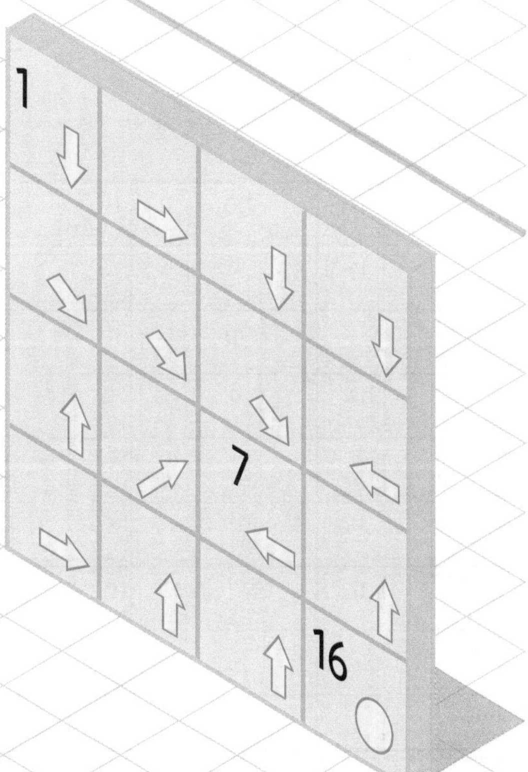

75

What number should replace the question mark?

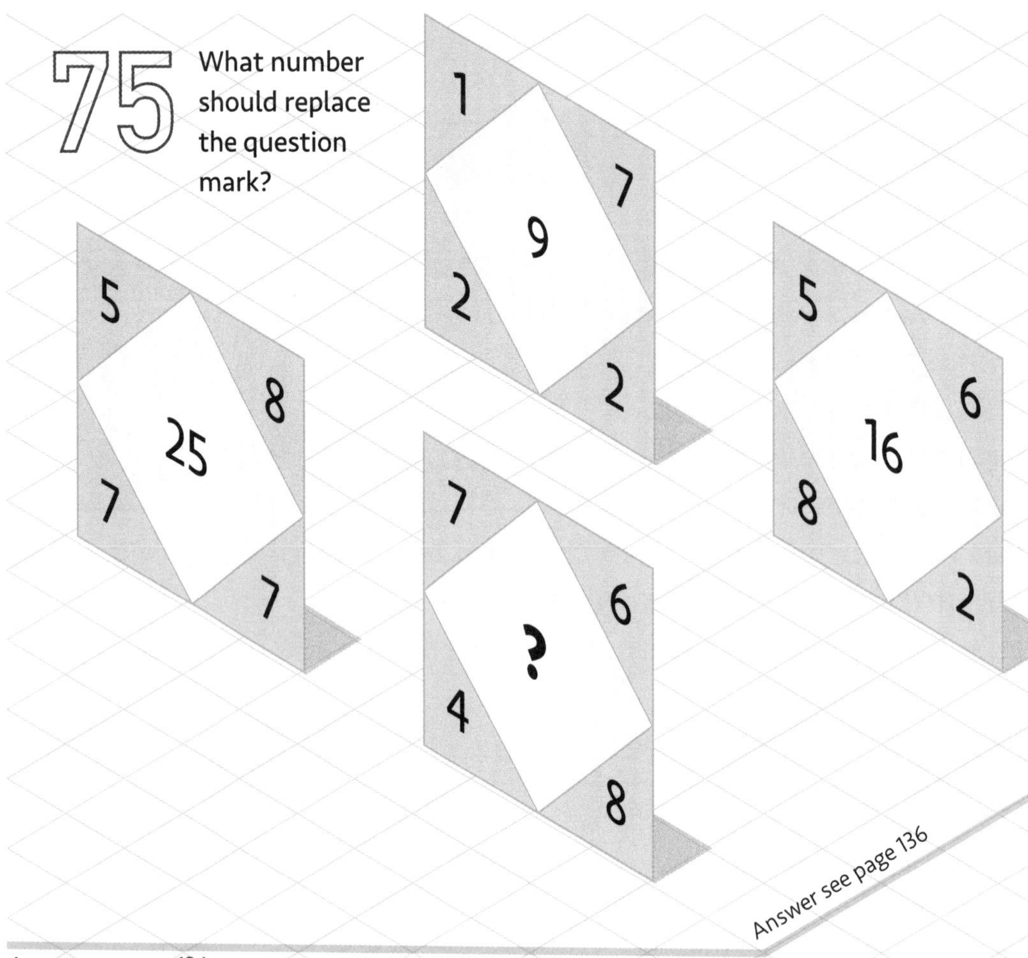

Answer see page 136

76

Complete the grid below so that every row, column, and 3x3 square each contains the digits 1-9 precisely once. The sum of the digits in each group of cells with a dotted outline must total the number in the group's top/left corner.

17	13	11		10	10	11		17
		13	9			7		
				11		10		
10	15	12	11	11		11	4	
					10		19	
8			9	11		11		
12		17			12	9	11	25
9			8					
6				15				

77

Decipher the names of several celebrities using the telephone dial as a guide.

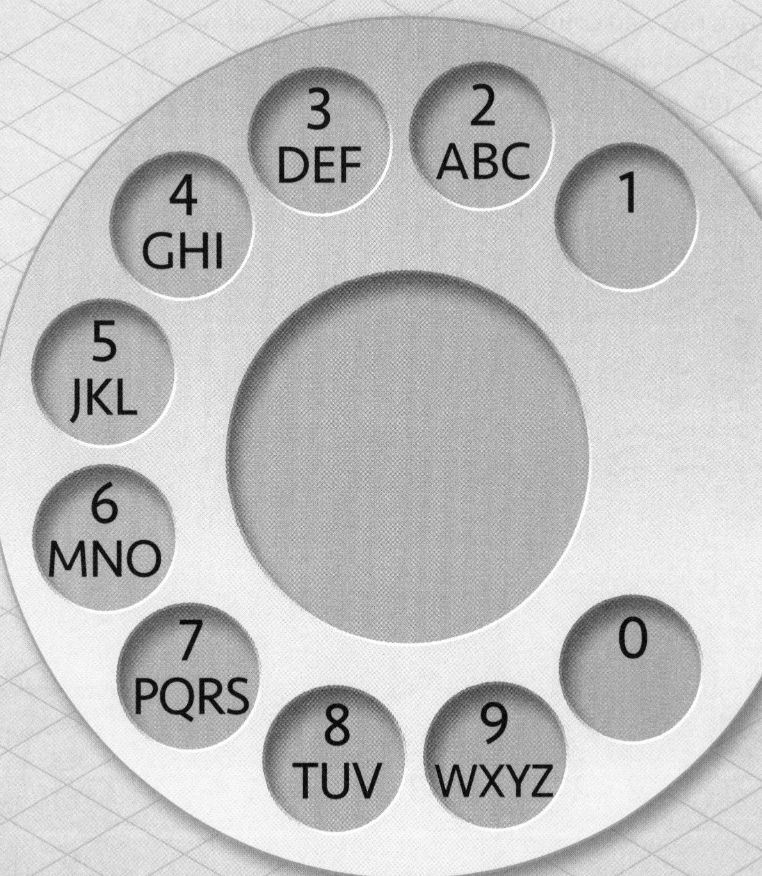

52637372626

5646693377

52832325467253

846343735

328438366268

2643546256543

Answer see page 136

Ten vessels are hidden in the grid below, four one cell ships, three two-cell ships, two three-cell ships, and one four-cell ship. Ships are positioned horizontally or vertically. No two ships are immediately adjacent to each other, including diagonally. The numbers next to each row and column show the total number of ship segments in that line. Identify the exact locations of all ten vessels. Some ship segments and/or spaces of empty ocean are shown to assist you.

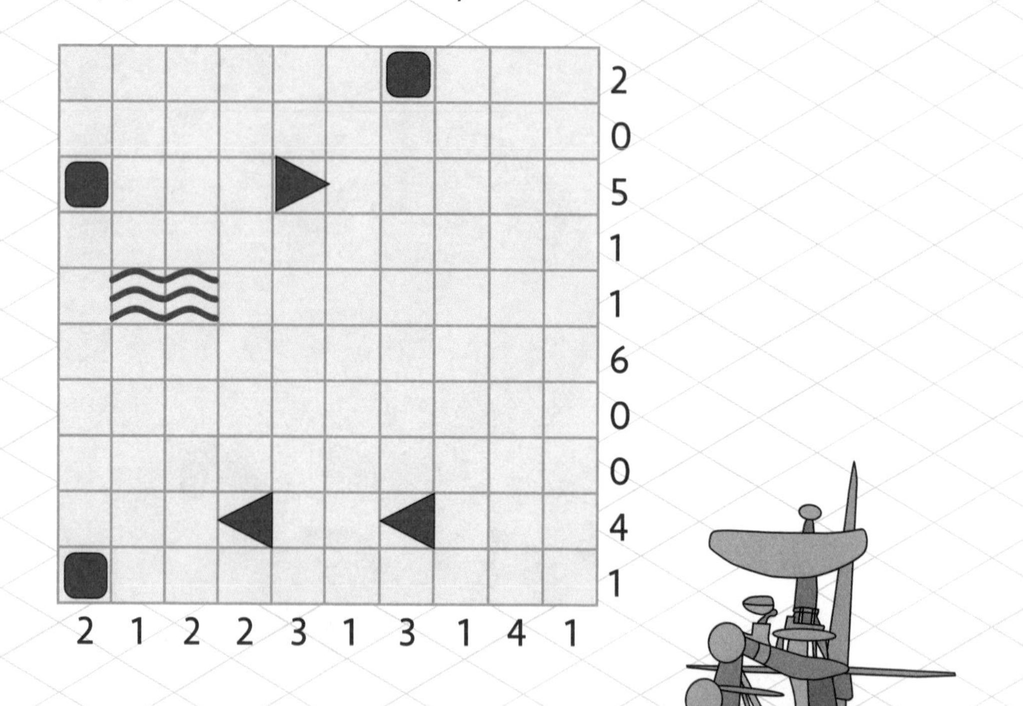

Answer see page 136

Assemble the pieces shown below into a square grid which reads the same across as it does downwards.

		6
5	6	1

5	8	3	1
8			

6	4
4	3

2
5
3

8	5	7
3	4	

		0
1	9	2

9	3	5

		9
4	9	3
		5

0	3
3	9
5	8

	5	
2	7	0
	9	

	2	
2	5	3
		5

Answer see page 136

Fill in the missing plus, minus, multiplication, division, and/or factorial signs to make the equation below correct, performing all calculations strictly in the order they appear on the page.

11 5 4 7 23 7 16 = 19

Answer see page 136

Answer see page 136

Are the following statements true or false?

i. There are no radioactive isotopes of aluminium.
ii. Lizards can be found on every continent on Earth.
iii. Miami is the capital of Florida.
iv. Pervez Musharraf is a former ruler of Afghanistan.
v. Pi, the ratio of a circle's diameter to it's circumference, is a rational number.
vi. Poznan is a city in Poland.
vii. Some dice have twelve sides.
viii Some mimosas can close up quickly when touched.
ix. The constellation of Columba represents a dove.
x. The number zero was invented in Arabia in the 9th century AD.

82

Which two cubes show three identical faces to each other?

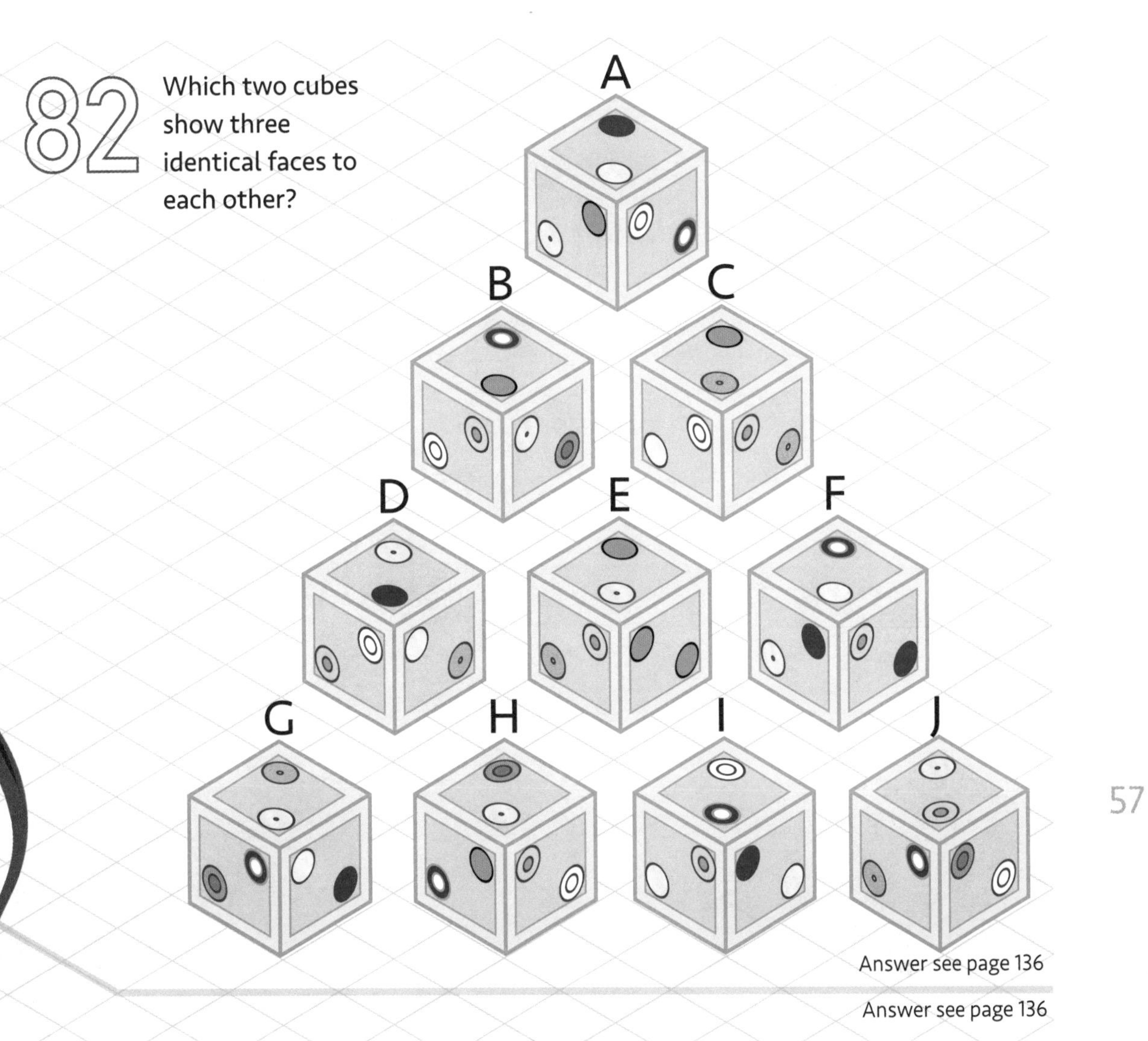

Answer see page 136

Answer see page 136

83

Using six straight lines, none of which touch an edge of the box, divide the design below into five sections, each containing precisely sixteen circles.

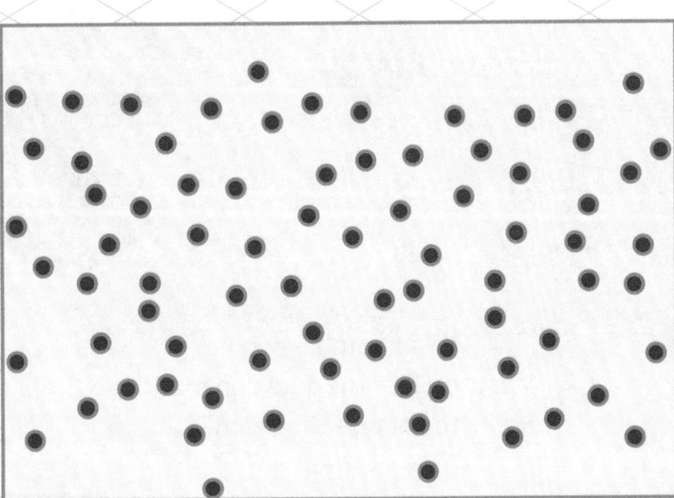

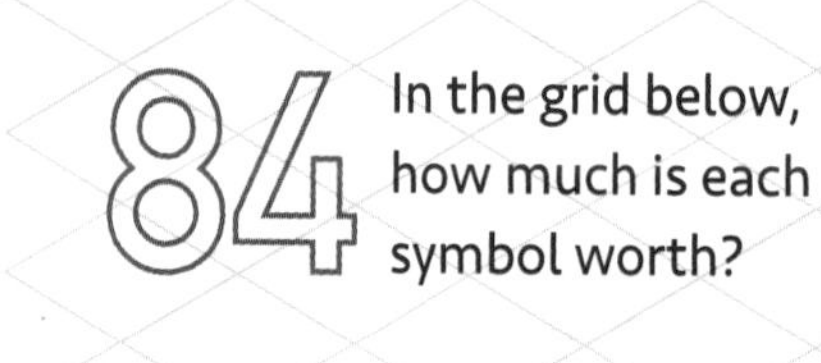

84

In the grid below, how much is each symbol worth?

23

17

12

18

15

16

Answer see page 136

18

?

85

What number should replace the question mark to balance the beam?

86

Complete the grid below so that each number shown forms part of a group of horizontally and/or vertically connected cells. The number of cells in the group must be the same as the number shown on the grid. So a '2' indicates a group that is a pair of two cells. No group shares a horizontal or vertical boundary with another group of the same size/number. Every group of cells has at least one number shown.

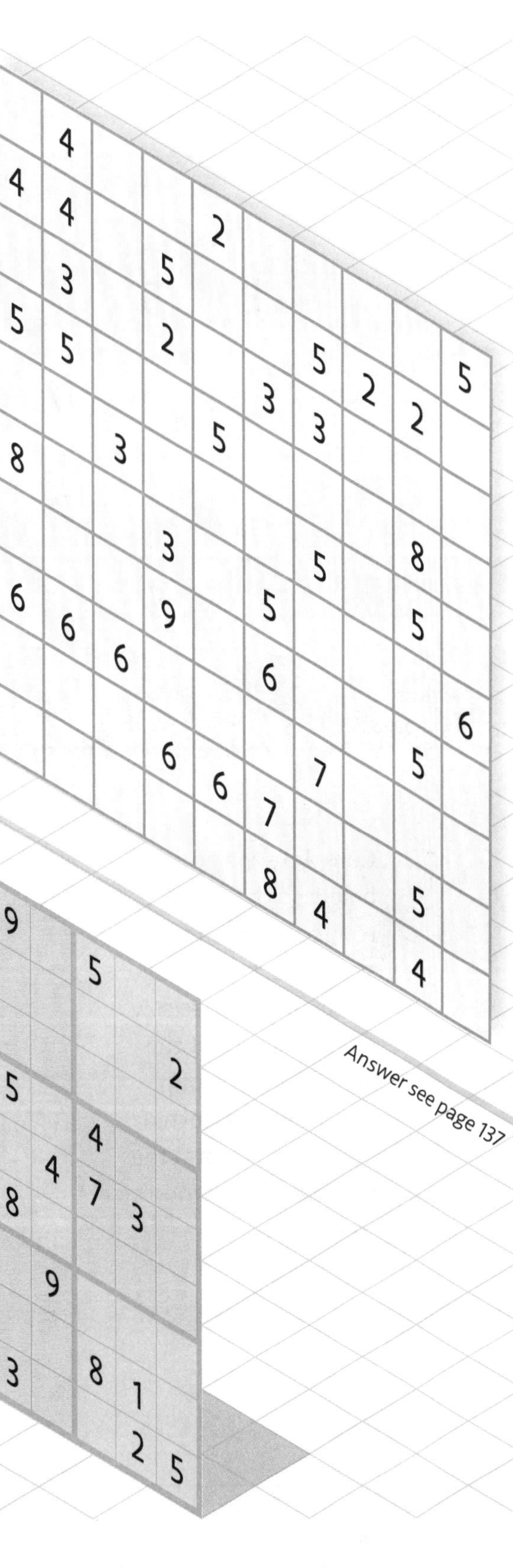

Answer see page 136

87

Complete the grid below so that every row, column, and 3x3 square each contains the digits 1-9 precisely once.

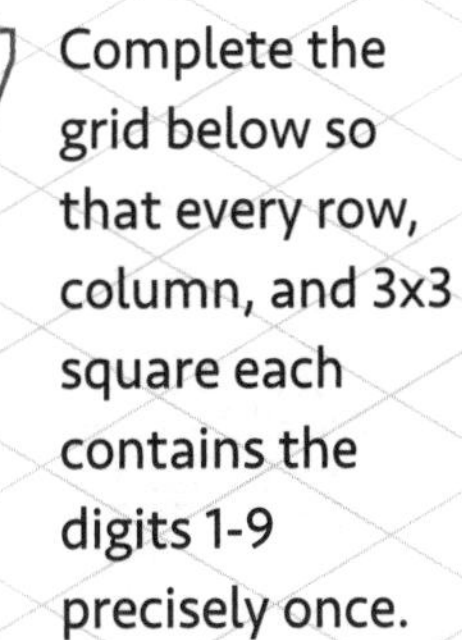

Answer see page 137

What number should replace the question mark?

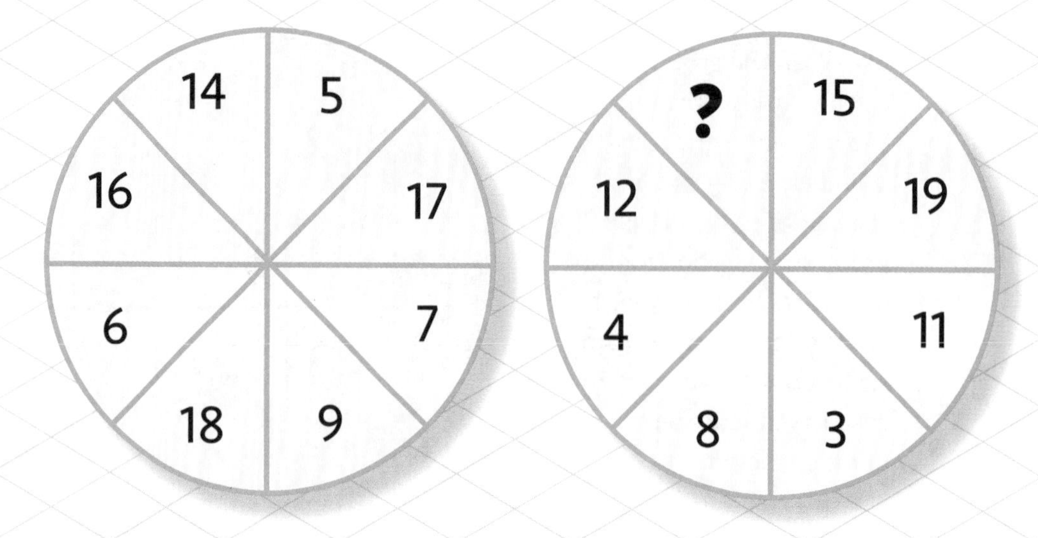

Answer see page 137

Answer see page 137

Complete the grid below so that every row, column, and 3x3 square each contains the digits 1-9 precisely once. The sum of the digits in each group of cells with a dotted outline must total the number in the group's top/left corner.

22			11	10	5	11		20
9		4				9		
11	13		14	11			6	
				16				11
12	4	13	7		14		13	
			10		12			7
9		9	9		18			
10			19	13	17		11	7
8								

90

Which symbols are missing from the grid below?

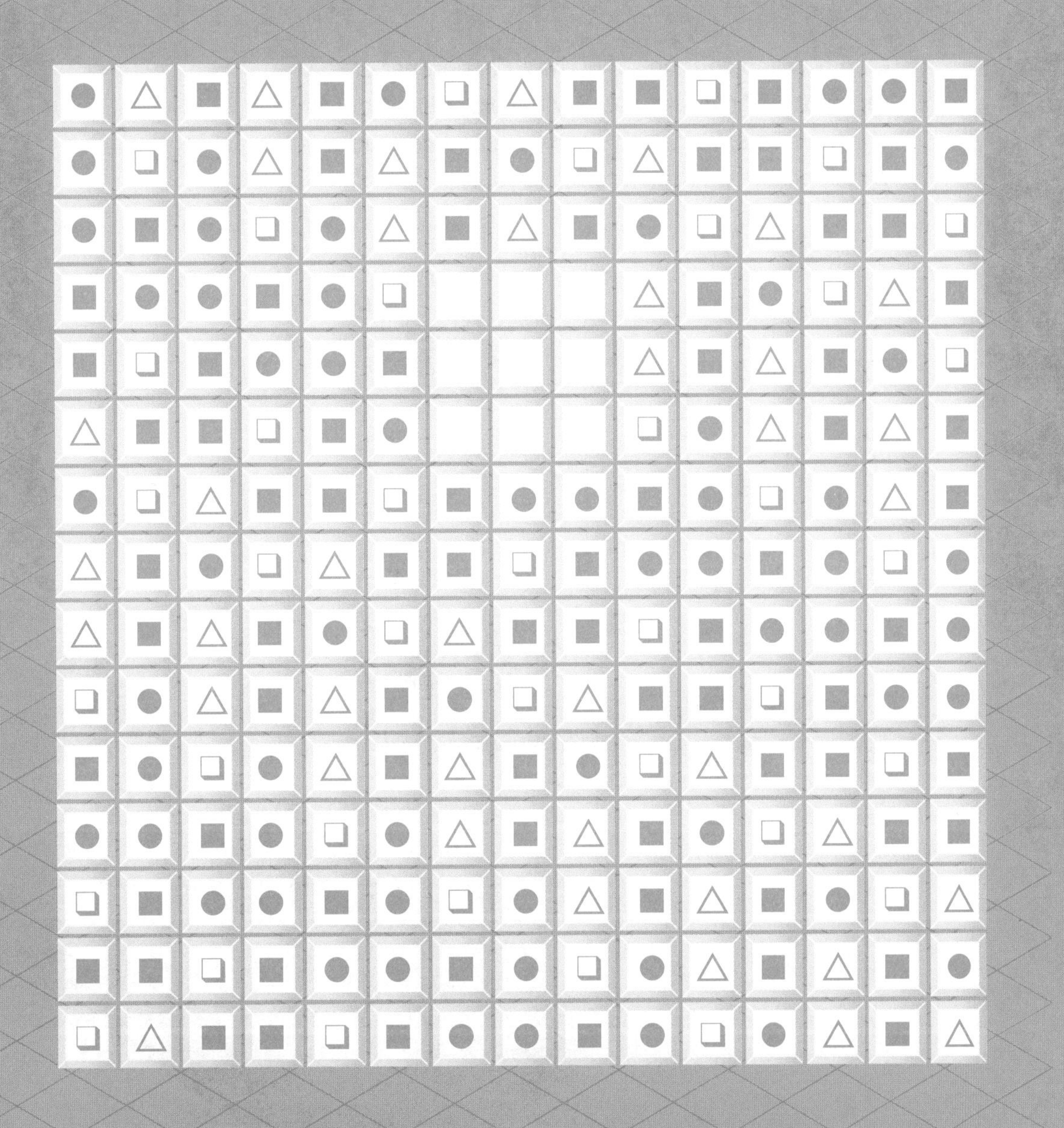

Answer see page 137

Ten vessels are hidden in the grid below, four one cell ships, three two-cell ships, two three-cell ships, and one four-cell ship. Ships are positioned horizontally or vertically. No two ships are immediately adjacent to each other, including diagonally. The numbers next to each row and column show the total number of ship segments in that line. Identify the exact locations of all ten vessels. Some ship segments and/or spaces of empty ocean are shown to assist you.

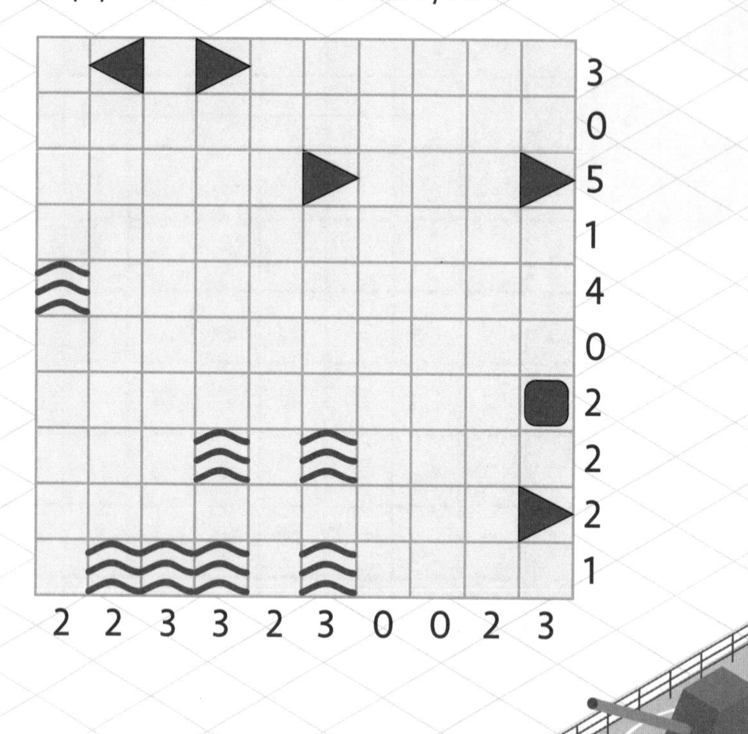

Answer see page 137

92

In each square, the arrow shows the direction you must move in. The numbers in some squares show that square's position in the correct sequence of moves. Move from top left to bottom right, visiting each square in the grid exactly once.

1

16

Answer see page 137

93

Which of the four pieces A to D fits to complete the shape?

A B C D

Answer see page 137

Decipher the names of several celebrities using the telephone dial as a guide.

78737847468
339273667866
5225642465766
2426646482886
27823945547
52637622869

Answer see page 137

In the grid below, how much is each symbol worth?

Answer see page 137

96

The pieces can be assembled into a regular geometric shape. What is it?

Answer see page 137

Complete the grid below so that every row, column, and 3x3 square each contains the digits 1-9 precisely once. The sum of the digits in each group of cells with a dotted outline must total the number in the group's top/left corner.

Answer see page 137

98 The pieces can be assembled into a regular geometric shape. What is it?

Answer see page 137

In the grid below, how much is each symbol worth?

21

18

20

22

Answer see page 137

7
2 5
8
1 6 2
7 3 6
6 2
1 8
6 5 4
9
8 5 1 2
1 8 6 3
4
2

Answer see page 137

100

Complete the grid below so that every row, column, and 3x3 square each contains the digits 1-9 precisely once.

Fill in the missing plus, minus, multiplication, division, and/or factorial signs to make the equation below correct, performing all calculations strictly in the order they appear on the page.

10 15 11 9 9 23 14 = 83

Answer see page 137

The pieces can be assembled into a regular geometric shape. What is it?

Answer see page 137

103

In the grid below, how much is each symbol worth?

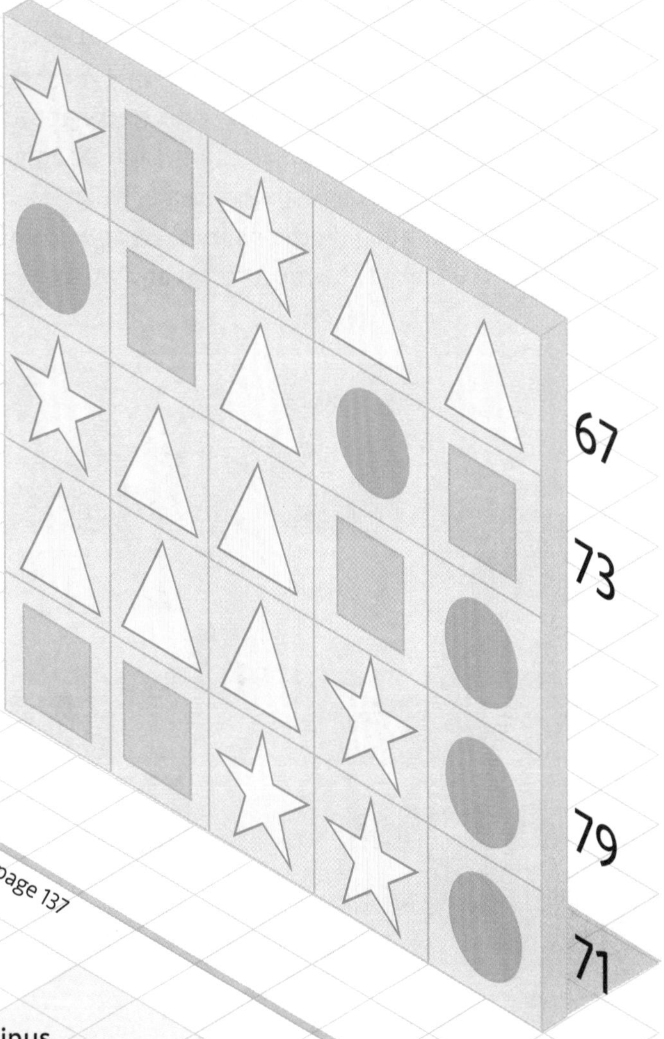

67

73

79

71

Answer see page 137

104

Fill in missing plus, minus, multiplication, division, and or factorial signs to make the equation below correct, performing all calculations strictly in the order they appear on the page.

20 1 23 7 16 20 4 = 265

Answer see page 137

Complete the grid below so that each unbroken horizontal and vertical stretch of light cells sums to the total indicated in the cell to the left or above the stretch respectively. Each cell may contain only the digits 1 – 9, and no digit may be repeated in any given stretch of cells.

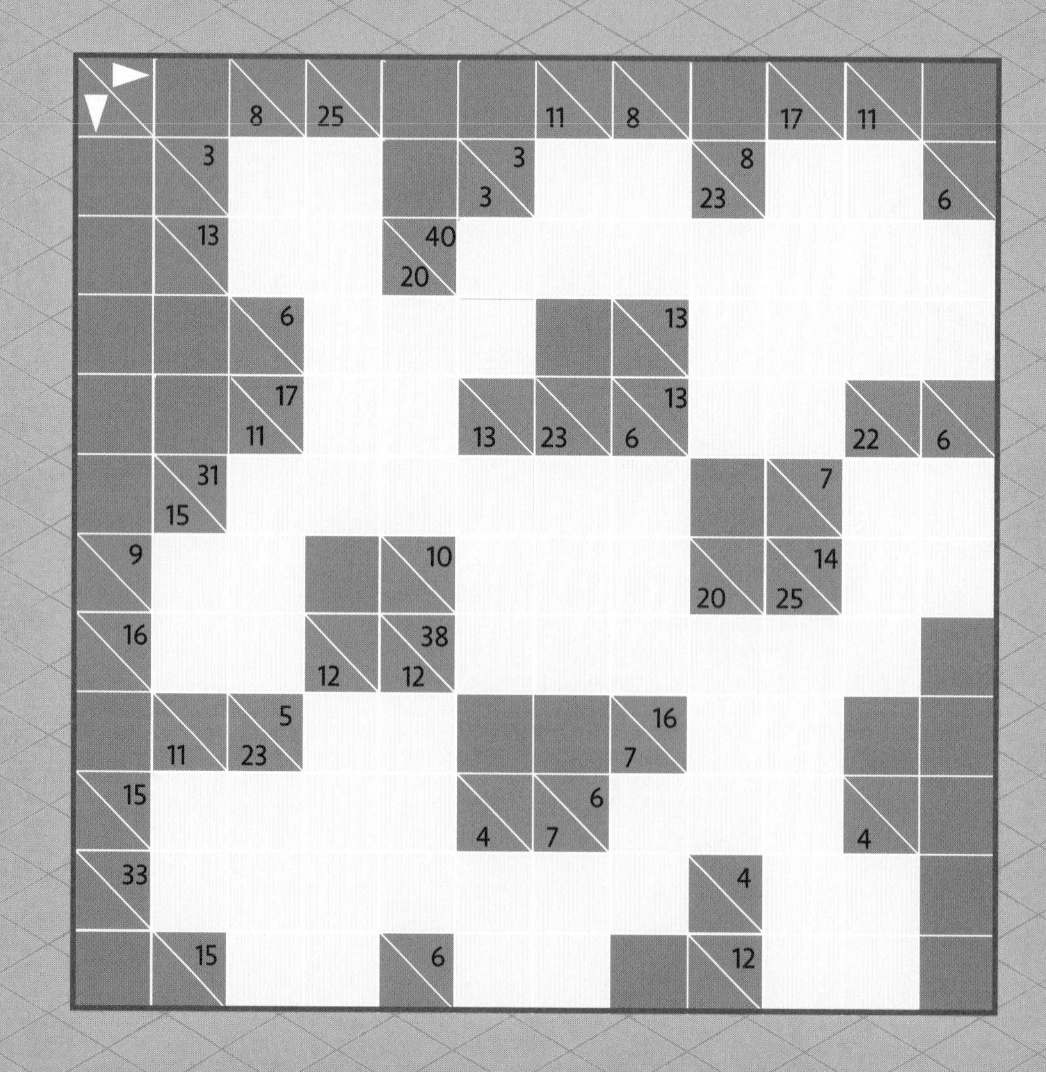

Answer see page 137

106

What number should replace the question mark?

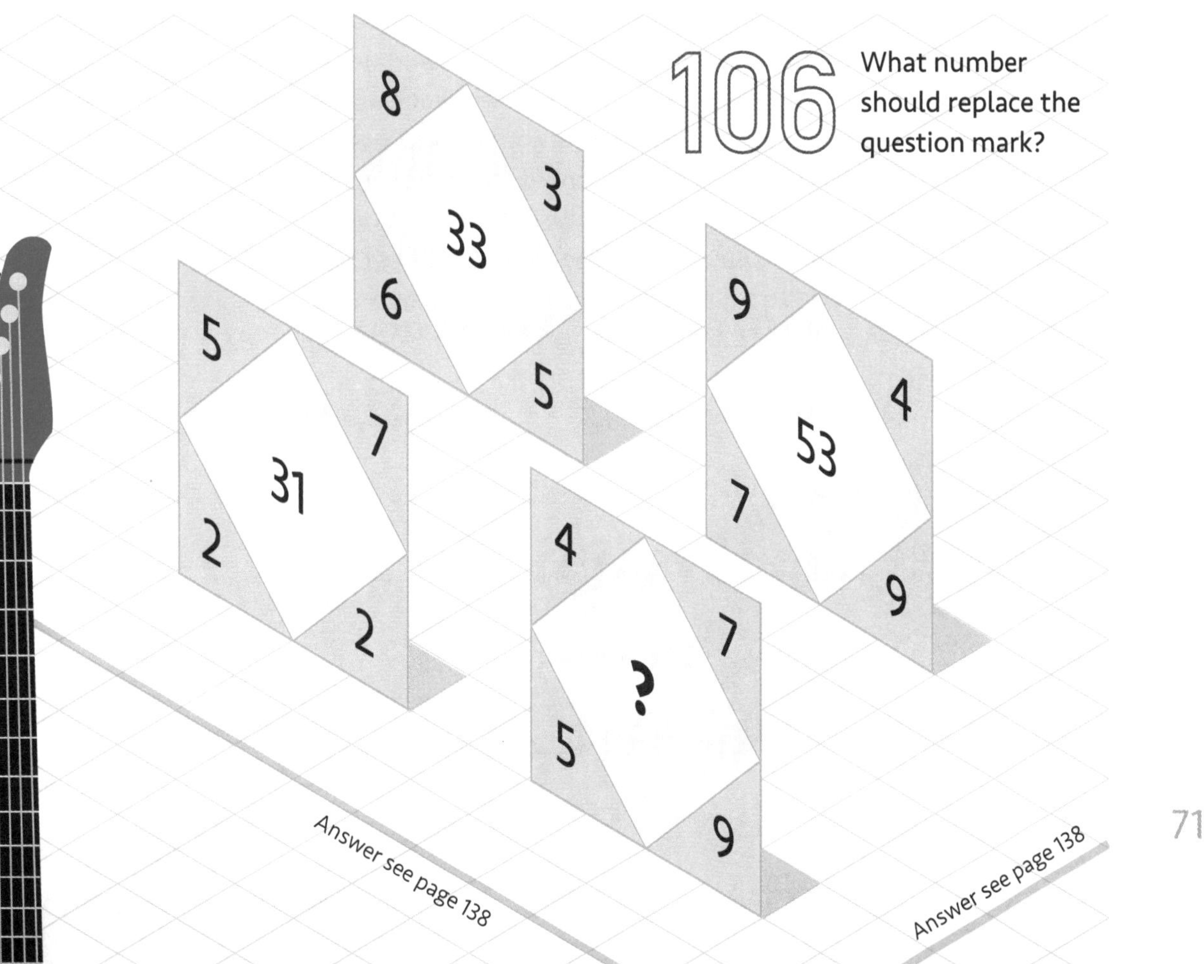

Answer see page 138

107

Jason likes Nirvana but not AC/DC. Sam likes Metallica but not Black Sabbath. Jennifer likes Red Hot Chili Peppers but not Green Day. Which of the following does Thomas like?

SONIC YOUTH

THE BEATLES

LED ZEPPELIN

PINK FLOYD

Answer see page 138

108

Ten vessels are hidden in the grid below, four one cell ships, three two-cell ships, two three-cell ships, and one four-cell ship. Ships are positioned horizontally or vertically. No two ships are immediately adjacent to each other, including diagonally. The numbers next to each row and column show the total number of ship segments in that line. Identify the exact locations of all ten vessels. Some ship segments and/or spaces of empty ocean are shown to assist you.

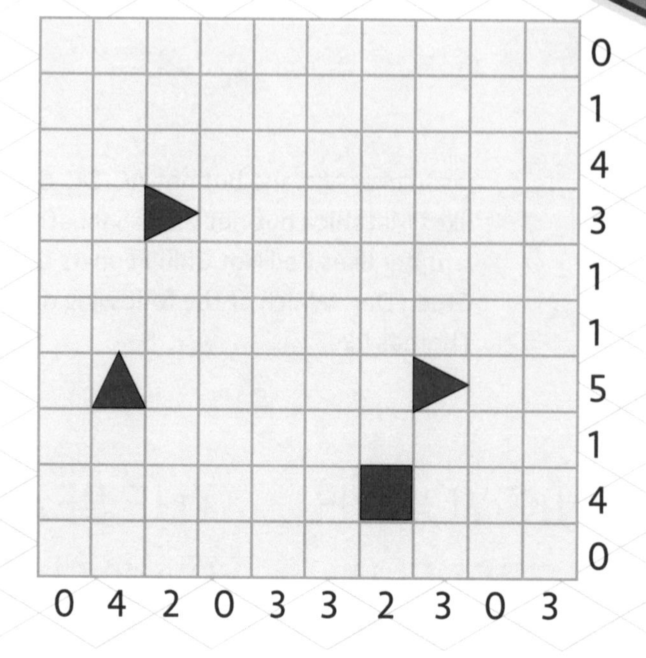

Answer see page 138

109

Which symbols are missing from the grid below?

●	■	●	△	△	△	■	△	△	■	■	●	●	●	■
△	△	■	■	●	●	●	■	●	△	△	△	■	△	△
■	●	△	△	△	■	△	△	■	■	●	●	●	■	●
△	■	■	●	●	●	■	●	△	△	△	■	△	△	■
●	△	△	△	■	△	△	■				●	■	●	△
■	■	●	●	●	■	●	△				△	△	■	■
△	△	△	■	△	△	■	■				■	●	△	△
■	●	●	●	■	●	△	△	△	■	△	△	■	■	●
△	△	■	△	△	■	■	●	●	●	■	●	△	△	△
●	●	●	■	●	△	△	△	■	△	△	■	■	●	●
△	■	△	△	■	■	●	●	●	■	●	△	△	△	■
●	●	■	●	△	△	△	■	△	△	■	■	●	●	●
■	△	△	■	■	●	●	●	■	●	△	△	△	■	△
●	■	●	△	△	△	■	△	△	■	■	●	●	●	■
△	△	■	■	●	●	●	■	●	△	△	△	■	△	△

Answer see page 138

From the information below, what was the school sport of the person with a scarred forearm?

The former gymnast had become a librarian, and was not Rebecca, who had a torn hamstring. The person who had a sprain was a sprinter at school, and was neither Kevin nor Elizabeth. The teacher was not named Daniel or Kelly. The former snowboarder had become a barista. The person with a broken arm did not play football at school. Kelly, who had been in a car crash, was not a librarian. Kevin was a cook, and did not have a forearm scar. The pharmacist was not a former pole vaulter.

Answer see page 138

111

The grid below shows the numbers on a full set of dominoes, from 0-0 to 9-9 inclusive, that have been pushed together horizontally and vertically to make a solid rectangle. Complete the grid to show where each domino lies.

Answer see page 138

Answer see page 138

112

What number should replace the question mark to balance the beam?

113

Which symbols are missing from the grid below?

Answer see page 138

114

Assemble the pieces shown below into a square grid which reads the same across as it does downwards.

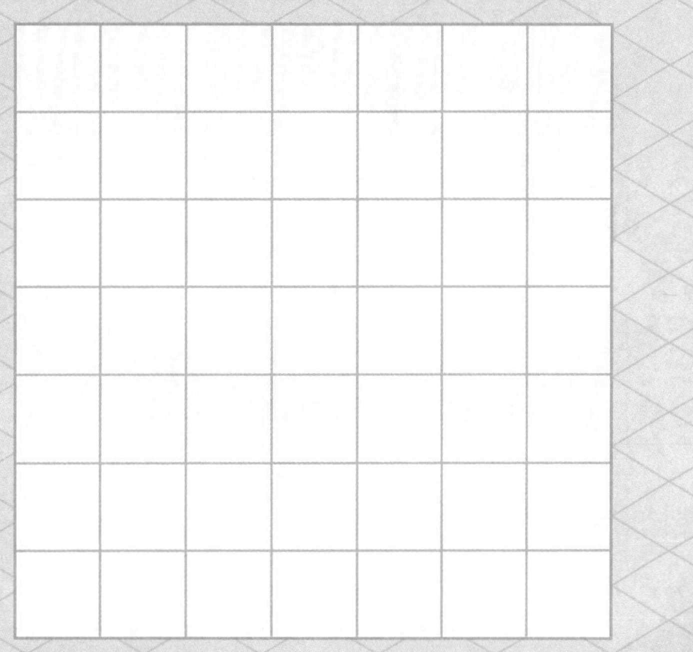

4	3
1	5
8	

	6
3	9
	6

4	8
7	
4	3

4	1
	5

4	6
5	9
	6

5	7	0	3

4	7	4

	5	
9	6	1

4	5	8
	9	
	7	

	6
	9
9	2

8	3
6	

7	0
0	
3	

4	1
	5

Answer see page 138

115

What number should replace the question mark?

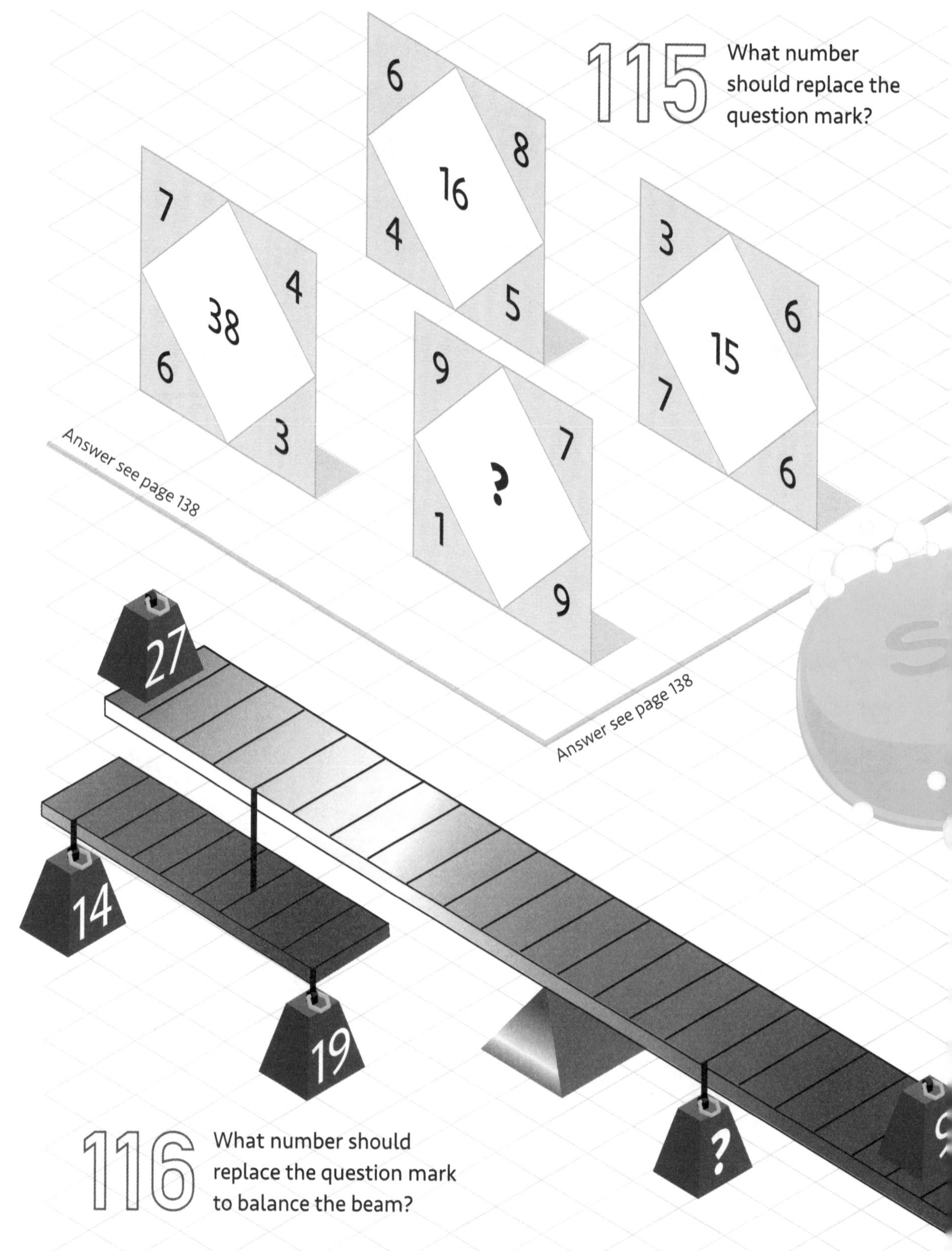

Answer see page 138

Answer see page 138

116

What number should replace the question mark to balance the beam?

117

Using six straight lines, divide the design below into six sections, each containing precisely fifteen circles.

Answer see page 138

118

Are the following statements true or false?

i. Chlorine means 'greenish-yellow'.
ii. Crocodile hearts have six chambers.
iii. Hypergammon is a variant of backgammon.
iv. In Italy, asphodel leaves are used to wrap a type of salami.
v. Lugo is a city in Portugal.
vi. Olympia is the capital of Washington.
vii. Soap was invented in roughly 2800BC.
viii. The constellation of Lacerta represents a lizard.
ix. Thomas Klestil was a former president of Austria.
x. Zero is an imaginary number.

Answer see page 138

Which symbols are missing from the grid below?

□	■	△	●	△	■	□	●	△	□	●	■	□	■	△
●	△	□	●	■	□	■	△	●	△	■	□	●	△	●
□	●	△	□	●	■	□	■	△	●	△	■	□	□	△
■	□	■	□	■	△	●	△	■	□	●	△	●	●	■
△	■	●	●	△	□	●	■	□	■	△	□	△	■	□
●	△	□	□	●	△				□	●	●	□	□	●
△	●	△	■	□	■				■	△	■	●	■	△
■	△	●	△	■	●				△	■	□	■	△	□
□	■	□	●	△	□	□	■	△	●	□	■	□	●	●
■	□	■	△	●	△	●	□	■	△	●	△	■	△	■
●	■	△	■	△	■	□	■	●	□	△	●	△	■	□
□	●	●	□	■	●	□	△	●	□	■	△	●	□	■
△	□	△	■	□	■	●	□	△	●	□	■	△	●	△
●	△	●	□	■	△	●	△	■	□	■	●	□	△	●
□	■	△	●	△	■	□	■	●	□	△	●	□	■	△

Answer see page 138

120

Complete the grid below so that every row, column, and 3x3 square each contains the digits 1-9 precisely once.

Answer see page 138

121

Which of the four pieces A to D fits to complete the shape?

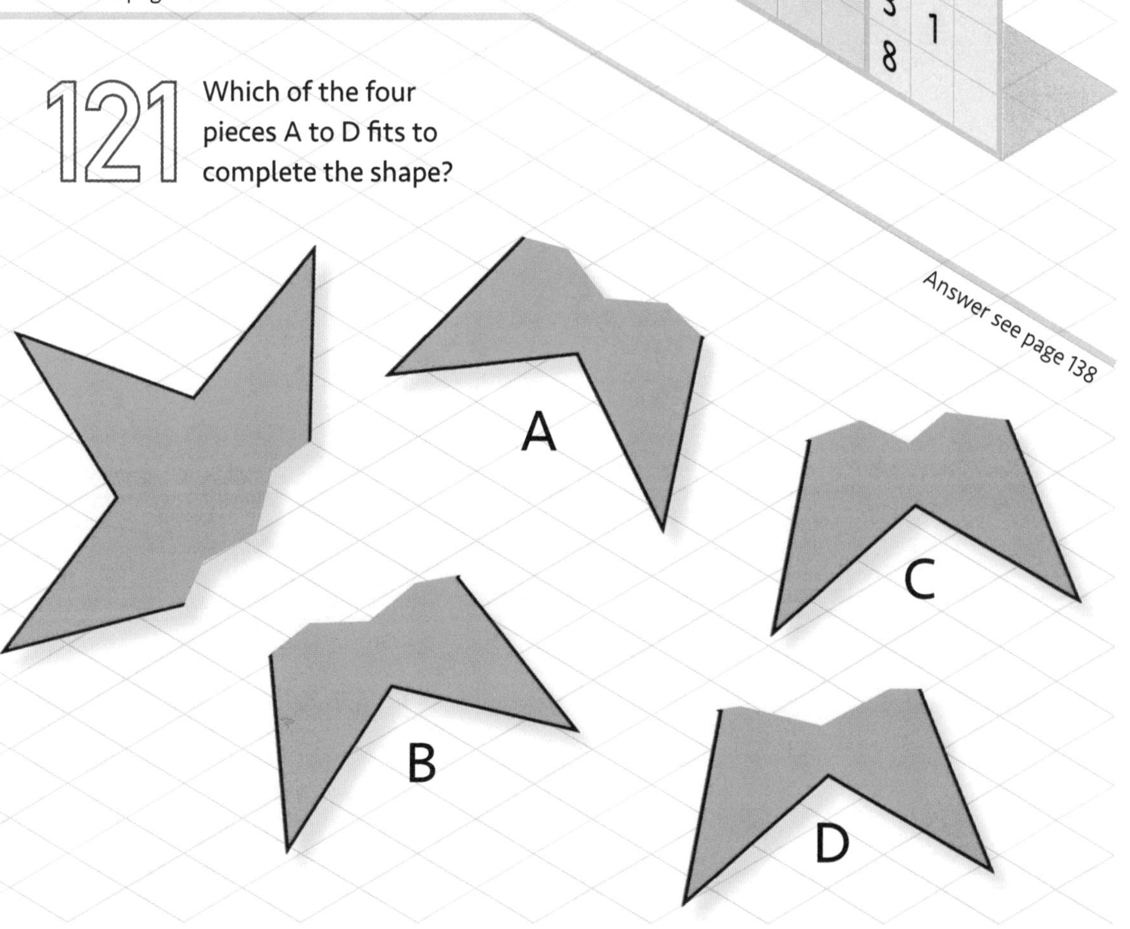

Answer see page 138

122

From the information below, what was the coffee served with the black forest gateau, and how much did it cost?

Either Scott or Jeffrey paid £5.50 and had an espresso. Jeffrey paid more than the person who had a blueberry muffin. Either Mary ate the black forest gateau and Richard had an americano, or Jeffrey ate the black forest gateau and Mary had the americano. Amanda, who got a ristretto, paid 50p more than the person who had a pain au chocolat, who was either Scott or Jeffrey. The person who ordered a latte paid less than the person who didn't have a black forest gateau, but who ordered an espresso. Someone had a cappuccino. The pain au chocolat meal cost more than the croissant meal. The amounts paid were £4.00, £4.50, £5.00, £5.50 and £6.00. Someone ordered a red velvet cake.

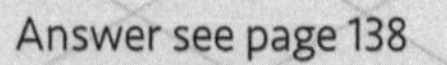

Answer see page 138

Using seven straight lines, divide the design below into seven sections, each containing precisely seven triangles.

124

What number should replace the question mark?

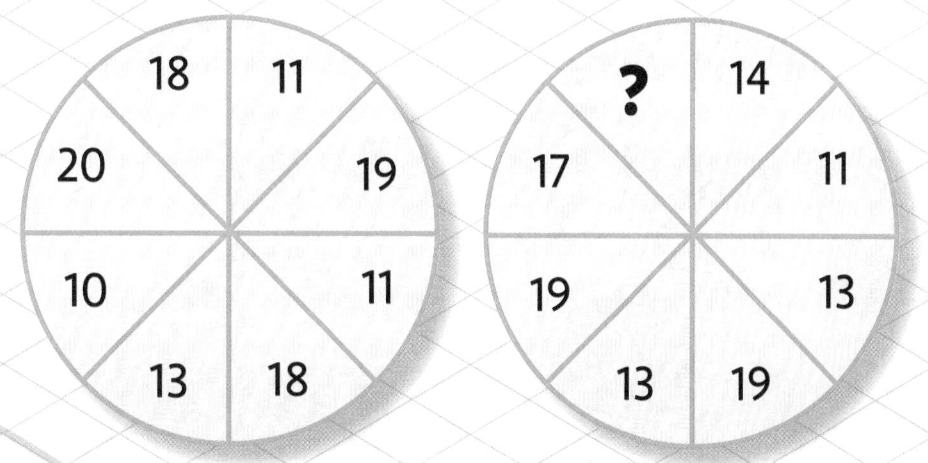

125

Which of the four pieces A to D fits to complete the shape?

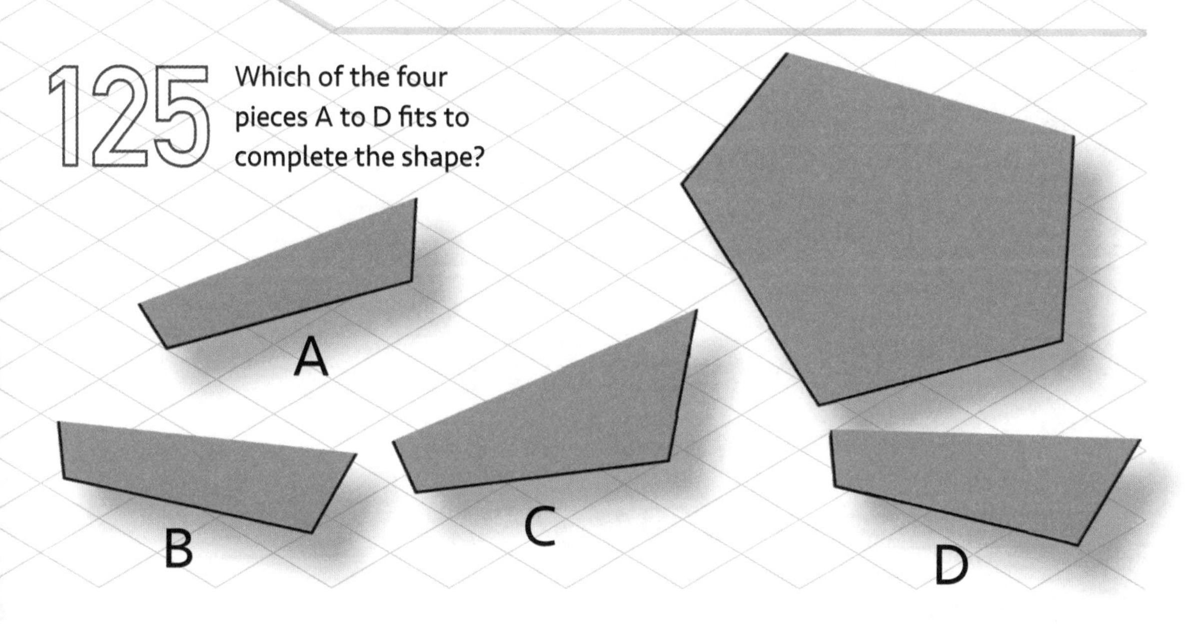

Decipher the names of several celebrities using the telephone dial as a guide.

2367845537

628832666

6936945766

266342842929

84625536

7624694554267

Answer see page 139

127

Assemble the pieces shown below into a square grid which reads the same across as it does downwards.

9
4
2

2 9
9 1

8
0
5
4

  4
1 7 9

9 4 7
  8

1 2
2
5

5 1 9
    3

5
8
1
2

1 2
5 4

4
6
1

3
9
3

4 2
9 3

9 4 6 1

Answer see page 139

Complete the grid below so that every row and column each contains the digits 1-6 precisely once. A cell with a chevron pointing into it is smaller than the cell on the other side of the chevron.

What number should replace the question mark?

Answer see page 139

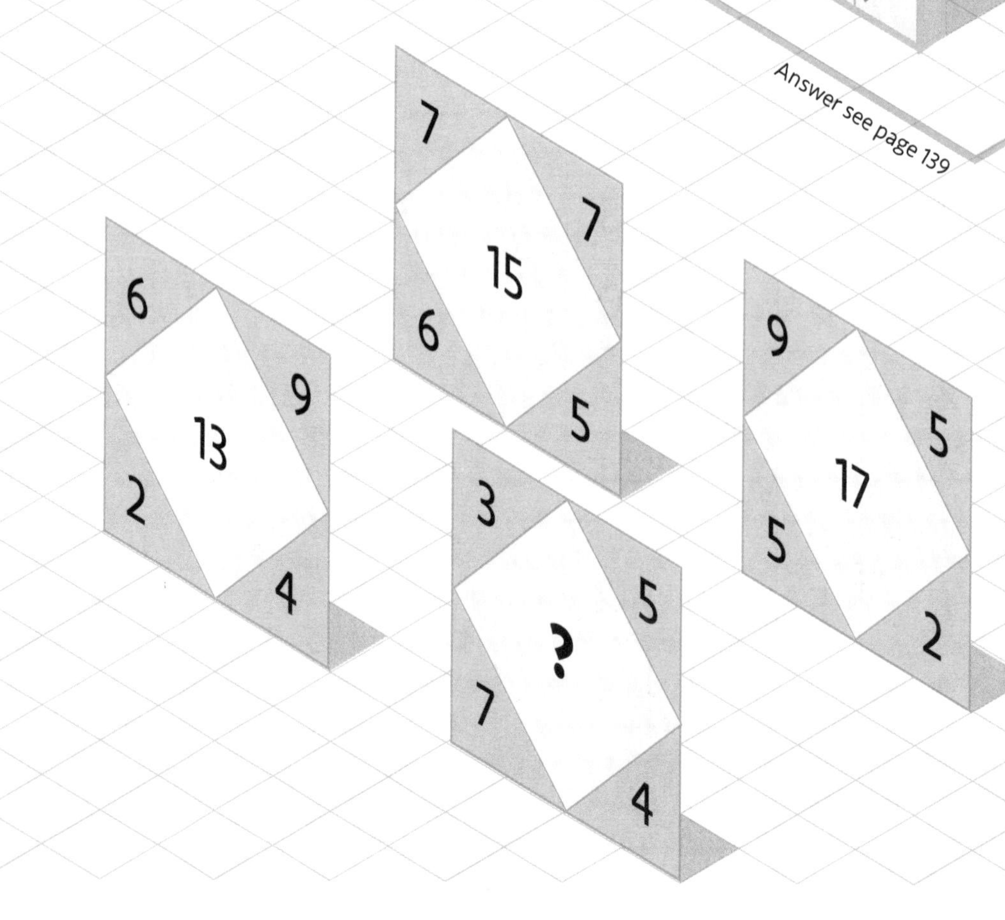

130

The grid below shows the numbers on a full set of dominoes, from 0-0 to 9-9 inclusive, that have been pushed together horizontally and vertically to make a solid rectangle. Complete the grid to show where each domino lies.

9	5	2	5	0	7	2	7	9	9	3
1	6	1	8	9	8	8	3	2	5	0
9	6	1	4	3	8	2	3	7	5	2
2	6	8	8	0	8	0	6	3	5	0
4	5	4	1	6	8	7	6	9	5	8
0	1	7	6	1	5	9	0	0	9	1
7	3	0	4	9	1	9	3	3	4	0
6	1	8	6	0	4	7	4	2	1	3
6	4	2	2	2	5	1	4	2	6	7
5	8	5	3	7	4	3	4	7	9	7

Answer see page 139

Complete the grid below so that every row and column each contains the digits 1-6 precisely once. A cell with a chevron pointing into it is smaller than the cell on the other side of the chevron.

Answer see page 139

Complete the grid below so that each unbroken horizontal and vertical stretch of light cells sums to the total indicated in the cell to the left or above the stretch respectively. Each cell may contain only the digits 1 – 9, and no digit may be repeated in any given stretch of cells.

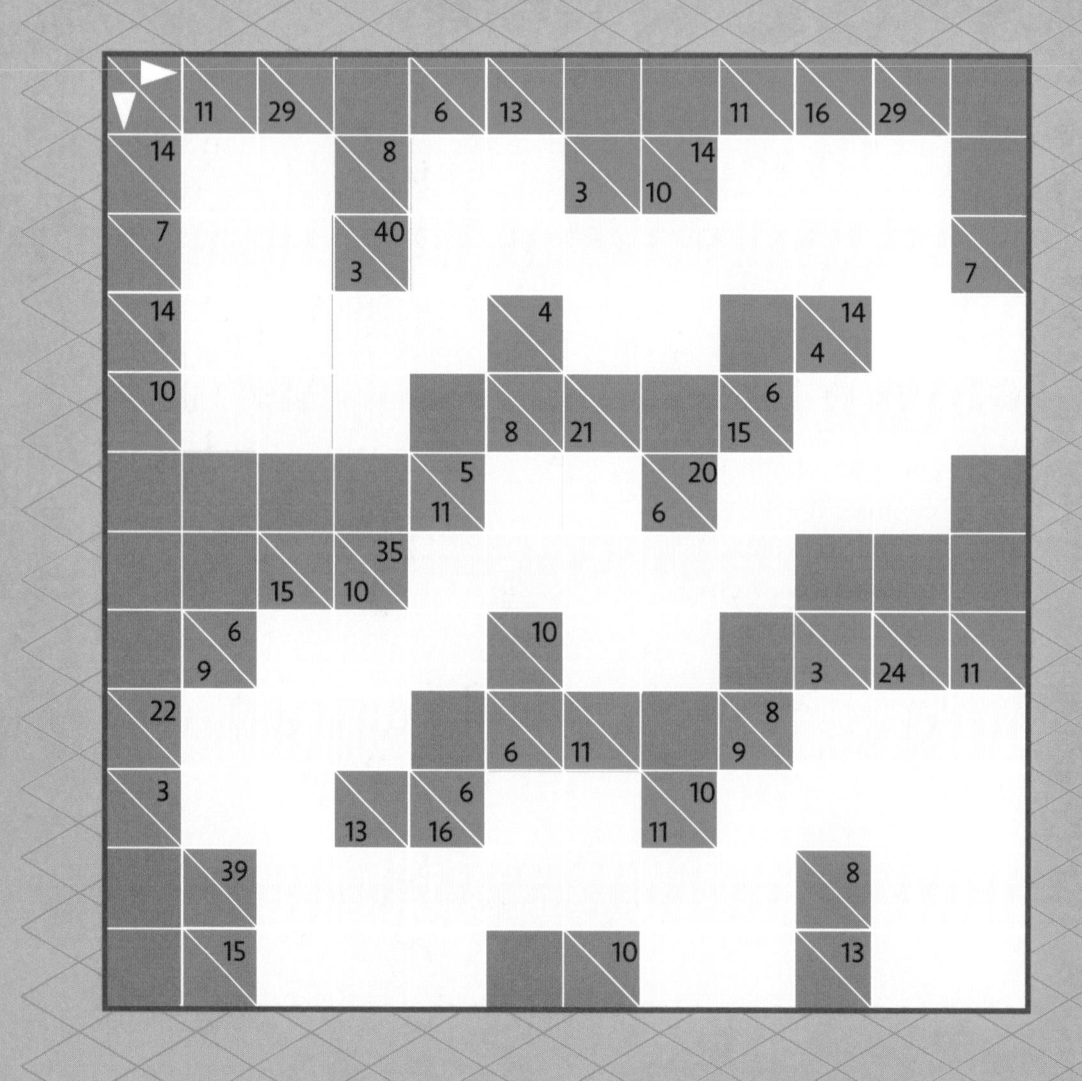

Answer see page 139

Complete the grid below so that every row and column each contains the digits 1-6 precisely once. A cell with a chevron pointing into it is smaller than the cell on the other side of the chevron.

Answer see page 139

Taylor likes Arsenal but not Chelsea. Deanna likes Southampton but not Portsmouth. Jayce likes Celtic but not Rangers. Which of the following does Frannie like?

EVERTON MANCHESTER UNITED

LIVERPOOL TRANMERE ROVERS

Answer see page 139

Answer see page 139

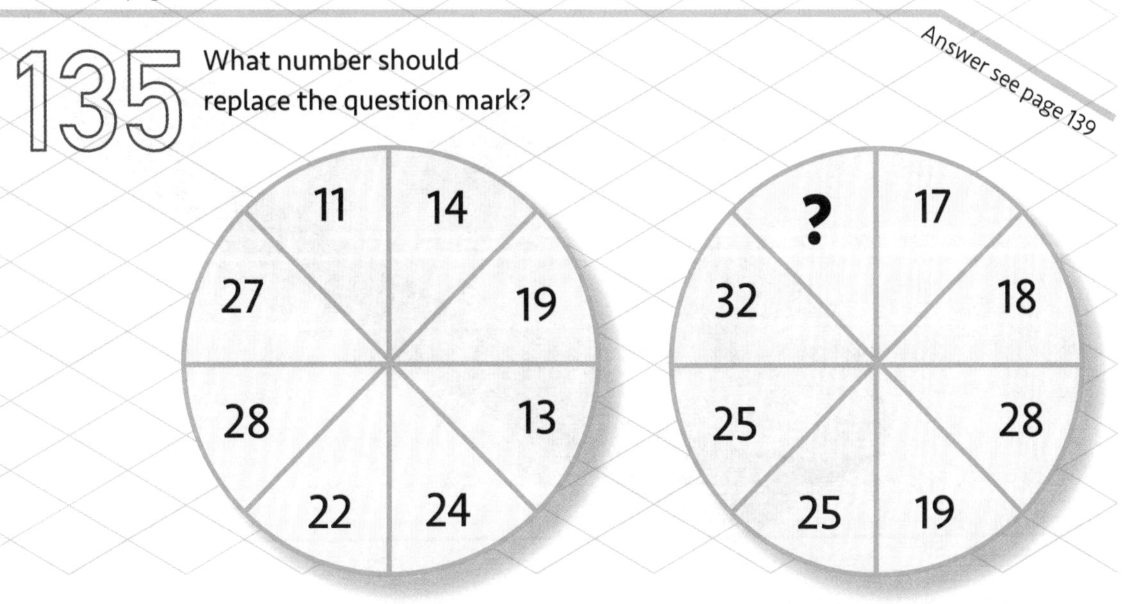

What number should replace the question mark?

Ten vessels are hidden in the grid below, four one cell ships, three two-cell ships, two three-cell ships, and one four-cell ship. Ships are positioned horizontally or vertically. No two ships are immediately adjacent to each other, including diagonally. The numbers next to each row and column show the total number of ship segments in that line. Identify the exact locations of all ten vessels. Some ship segments and/or spaces of empty ocean are shown to assist you.

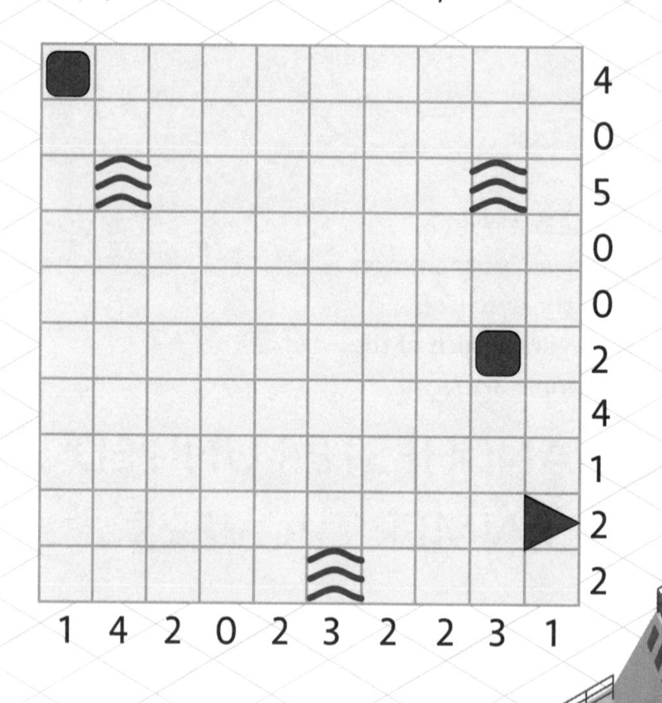

Answer see page 139

137

The pieces can be assembled into a regular geometric shape. What is it?

Answer see page 139

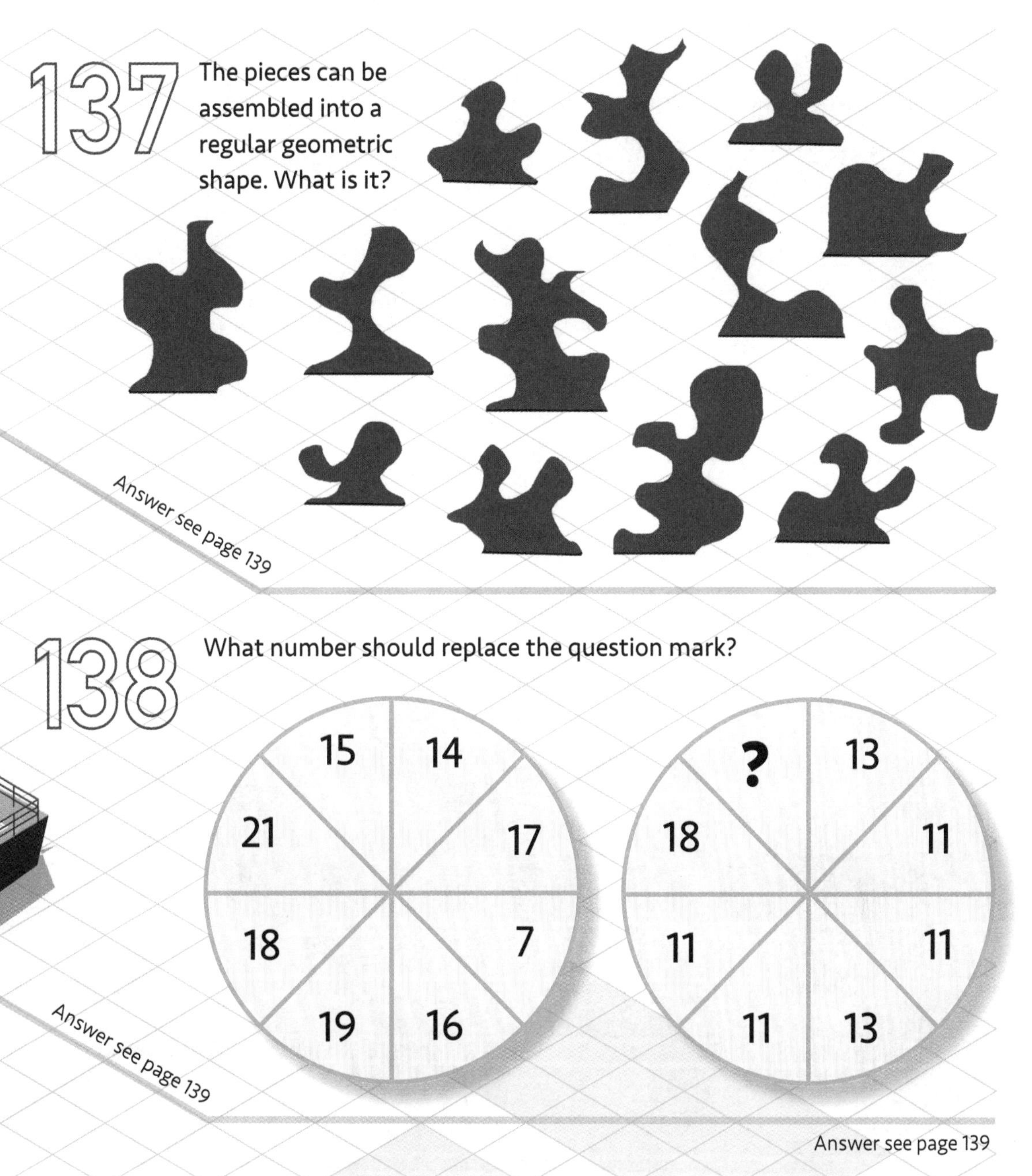

138

What number should replace the question mark?

Answer see page 139

Answer see page 139

139

Fill in the missing plus, minus, multiplication, division, and/or factorial signs to make the equation below correct, performing all calculations strictly in the order they appear on the page.

13 2 8 22 7 12 15 = 365

Complete the grid below so that each unbroken horizontal and vertical stretch of light cells sums to the total indicated in the cell to the left or above the stretch respectively. Each cell may contain only the digits 1 – 9, and no digit may be repeated in any given stretch of cells.

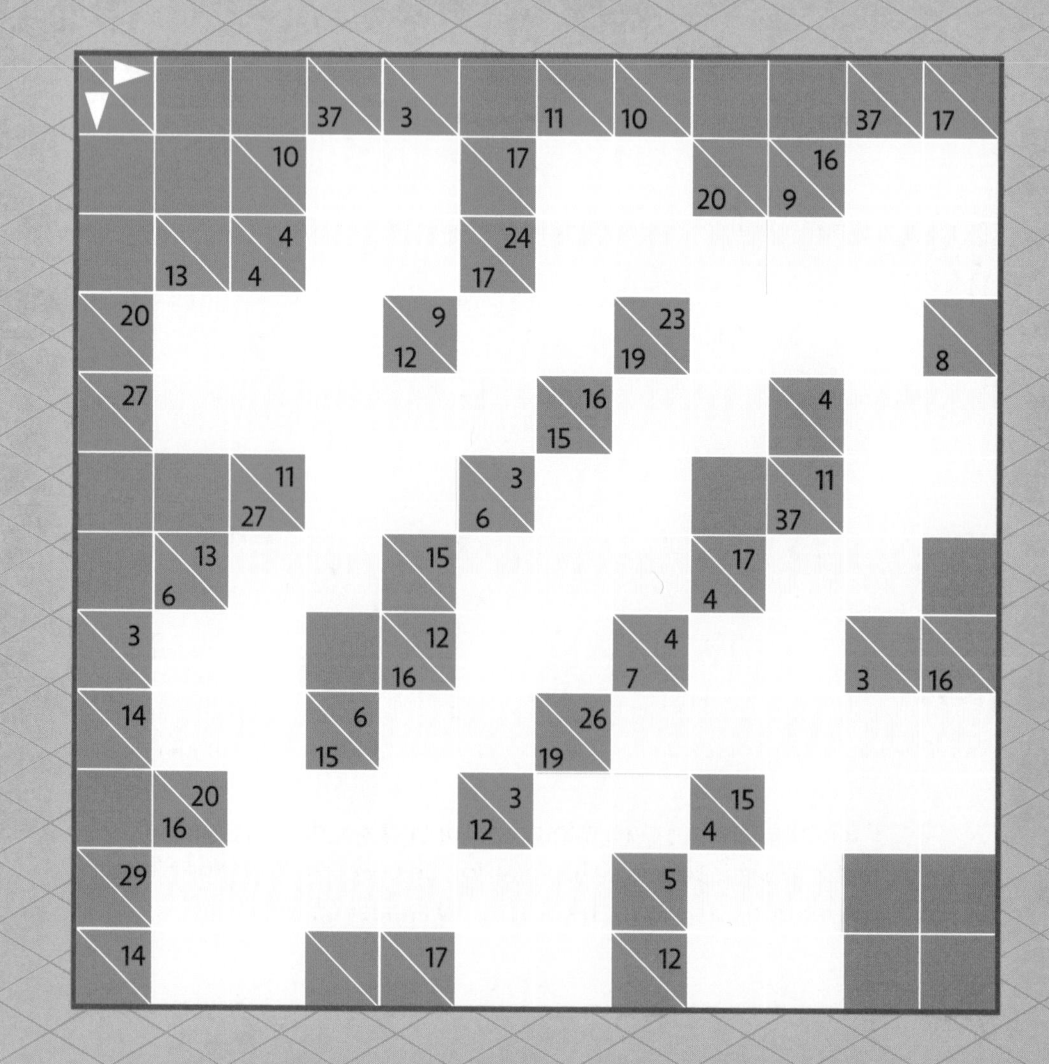

Answer see page 140

141

Connect each pair of identical numbers with a single continuous path running horizontally and/or vertically through the cells of the grid below. Paths may switch direction at the centre of a cell, but may not branch, loop back on themselves, or cross. When the grid is complete, each cell will contain a single path section.

10					6				
			13		11	3			
	2		2	10		12	7		
	8								
			9	8					
		11						3	
								7	
	5			5		12	1	1	6
	4			4					9
									13

Answer see page 140

142

Are the following statements true or false?

i. Argon is the fourth-most abundant gas in the Earth's atmosphere, after water vapour.
ii. Frogs have small tails.
iii. José de San Martin was the first President of Peru.
iv. Karpathos is a Greek island.
v. Morning glories all belong to the genus Convulvulus.
vi. Santa Fe is the capital of New Mexico.
vii. The constellation of Pavo represents a phoenix.
viii. The revolver was invented in the USA.
ix. The Sieve of Eratosthenes is a technique for finding prime numbers.
x. Yahtzee is played with six regular dice.

Answer see page 140

Which symbols are missing from the grid below?

△	□	△	□	●	△	●	△	□	△	□	●	△	●	□
□	●	□	△	△	△	□	□	●	□	●	□	●	△	△
●	△	●	□	●	●	△	●	△	●				△	□
△	●	□	●	□	□	□	□	△	△				●	●
△	□	△	△	△	△	●	△	●	●				□	△
●	△	□	△	□	□	△	□	□	□	●	△	●	△	●
□	□	●	●	●	●	●	●	△	△	△	△	□	□	□
△	●	△	□	□	□	□	△	□	□	△	●	△	●	△
□	△	△	△	△	△	△	●	●	●	●	□	□	□	□
●	△	●	□	□	□	□	□	△	△	□	△	●	△	●
△	●	□	●	●	●	●	△	●	△	△	□	△	□	□
●	□	△	□	△	△	□	□	□	●	□	●	△	●	△
□	△	□	△	△	●	△	●	△	□	●	□	●	△	□
△	□	●	□	●	□	□	△	□	△	△	△	□	●	●
□	●	△	●	□	△	●	△	●	□	●	□	△	□	△

Answer see page 140

Assemble the pieces shown below into a square grid which reads the same across as it does downwards.

7 8
0 2

8
0 9

5 7 0
    2

4 8 3

8
9
1
8

2 4
7 8

3 1
8 4

3 8
8 7

4
5 4

2
4
5 4

  7
7 2

1
9
3

3 8
1

4
0
9

Answer see page 140

Julie likes Milan but not Rome. Olivia likes Warsaw but not Krakow. Eric likes Kiev but not Odessa. Laurence likes Barcelona but not Madrid. Which of the following does Allan like?

SAINT PETERSBURG MOSCOW
VLADIVOSTOK PERM

Answer see page 140

146

Ten vessels are hidden in the grid below, four one cell ships, three two-cell ships, two three-cell ships, and one four-cell ship. Ships are positioned horizontally or vertically. No two ships are immediately adjacent to each other, including diagonally. The numbers next to each row and column show the total number of ship segments in that line. Identify the exact locations of all ten vessels. Some ship segments and/or spaces of empty ocean are shown to assist you.

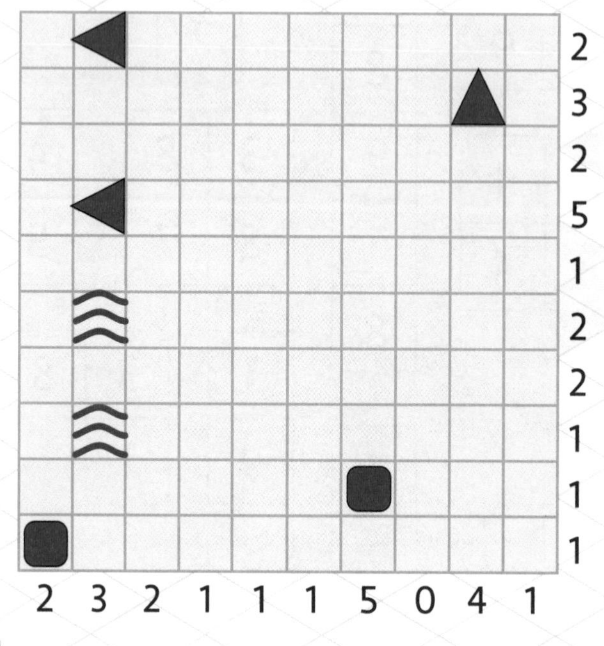

Answer see page 140

147

In the grid below, how much is each symbol worth?

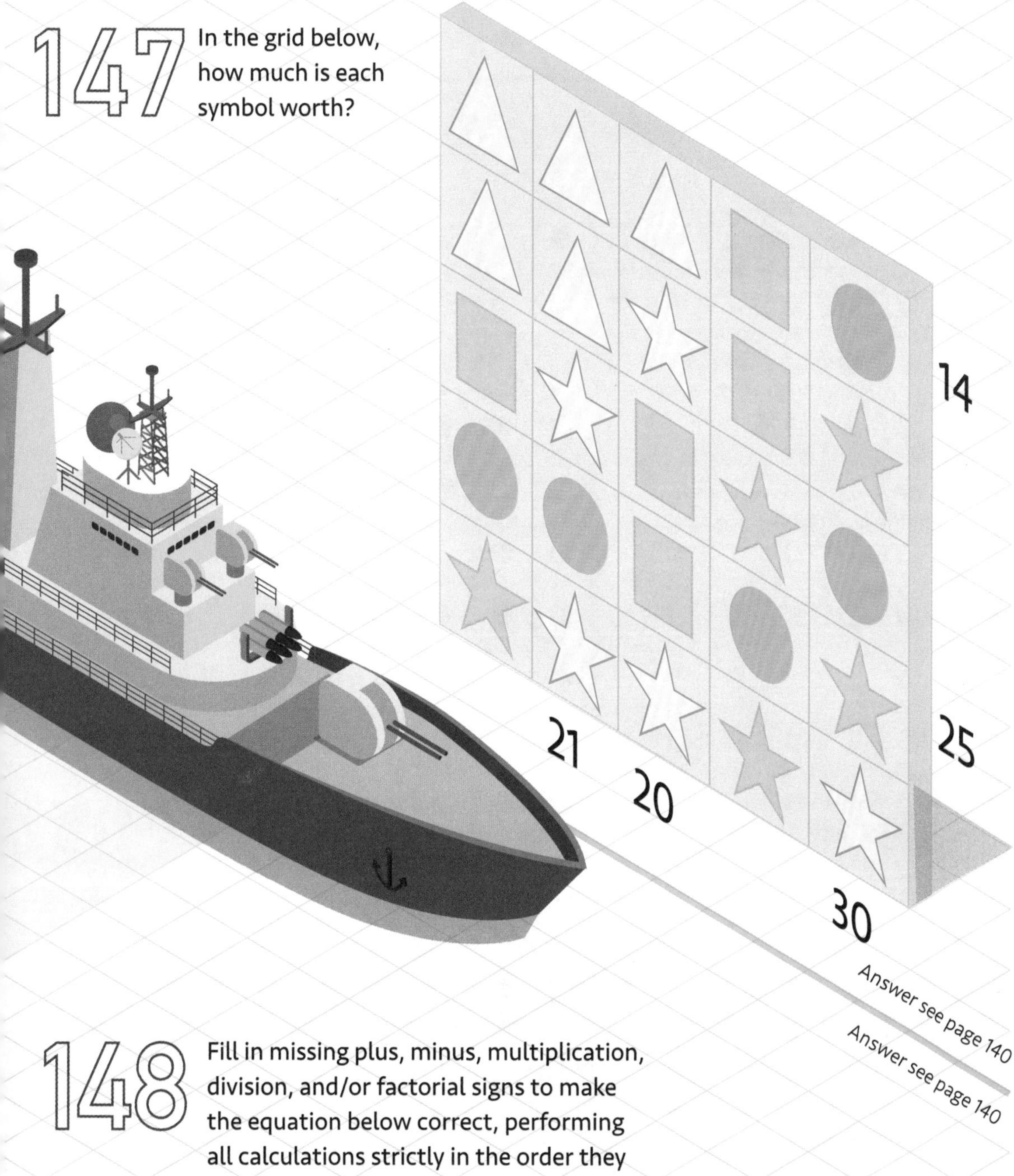

14

25

21

20

30

Answer see page 140

148

Fill in missing plus, minus, multiplication, division, and/or factorial signs to make the equation below correct, performing all calculations strictly in the order they appear on the page.

17 14 6 13 4 16 3 = 489

Answer see page 140

Which symbols are missing from the grid below?

Answer see page 140

150

The pieces can be assembled into a shape. What is it?

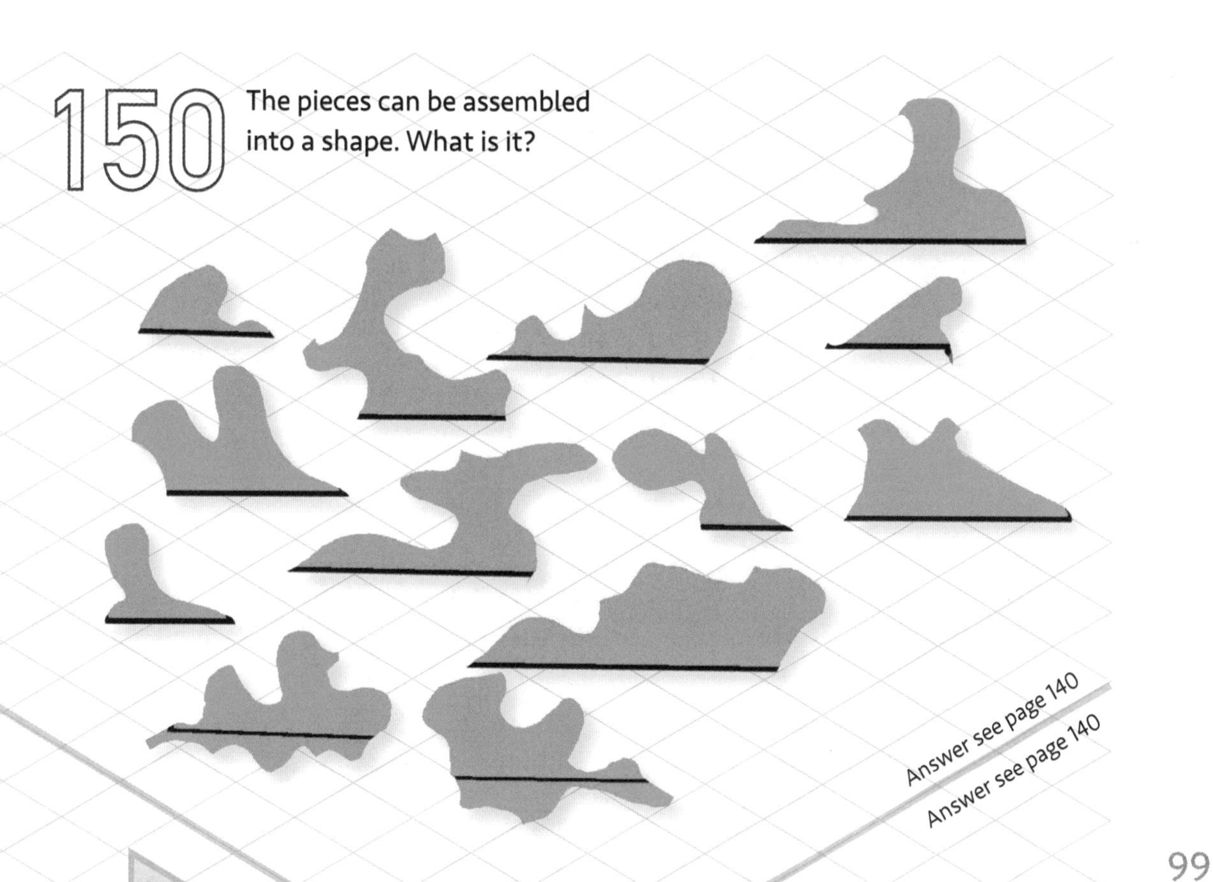

Answer see page 140

Answer see page 140

151

Complete the grid below so that every row, column, and 3x3 square each contains the digits 1-9 precisely once.

Complete the grid below so that each unbroken horizontal and vertical stretch of light cells sums to the total indicated in the cell to the left or above the stretch respectively. Each cell may contain only the digits 1 – 9, and no digit may be repeated in any given stretch of cells.

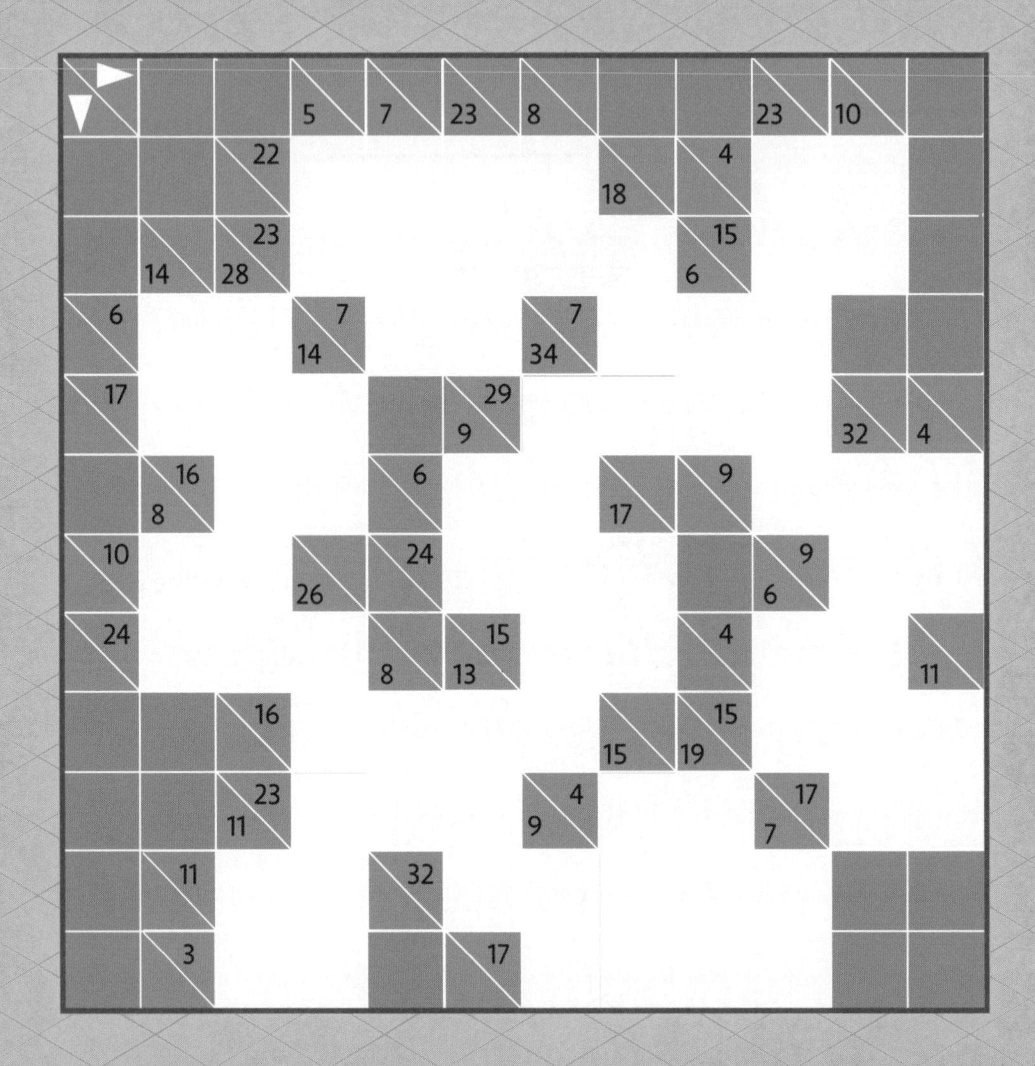

Answer see page 140

Complete the grid below so that every row and column each contains the digits 1-6 precisely once. A cell with a chevron pointing into it is smaller than the cell on the other side of the chevron.

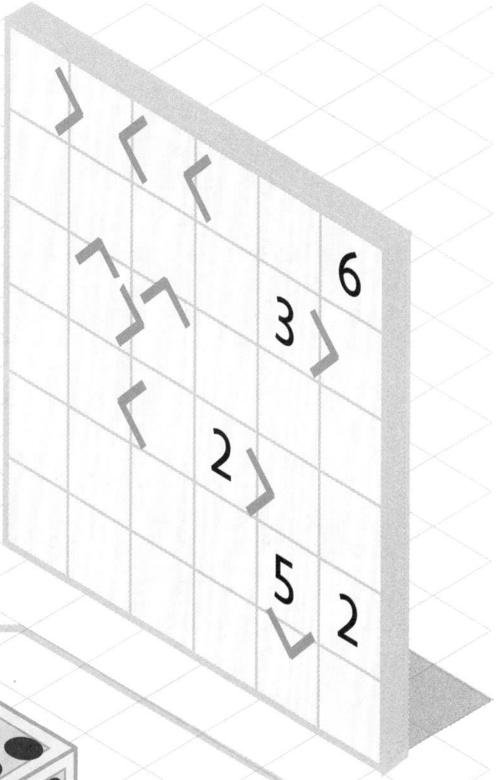

Answer see page 140

154

Two faces, on separate cubes, show identical symbols. To which cubes do they belong?

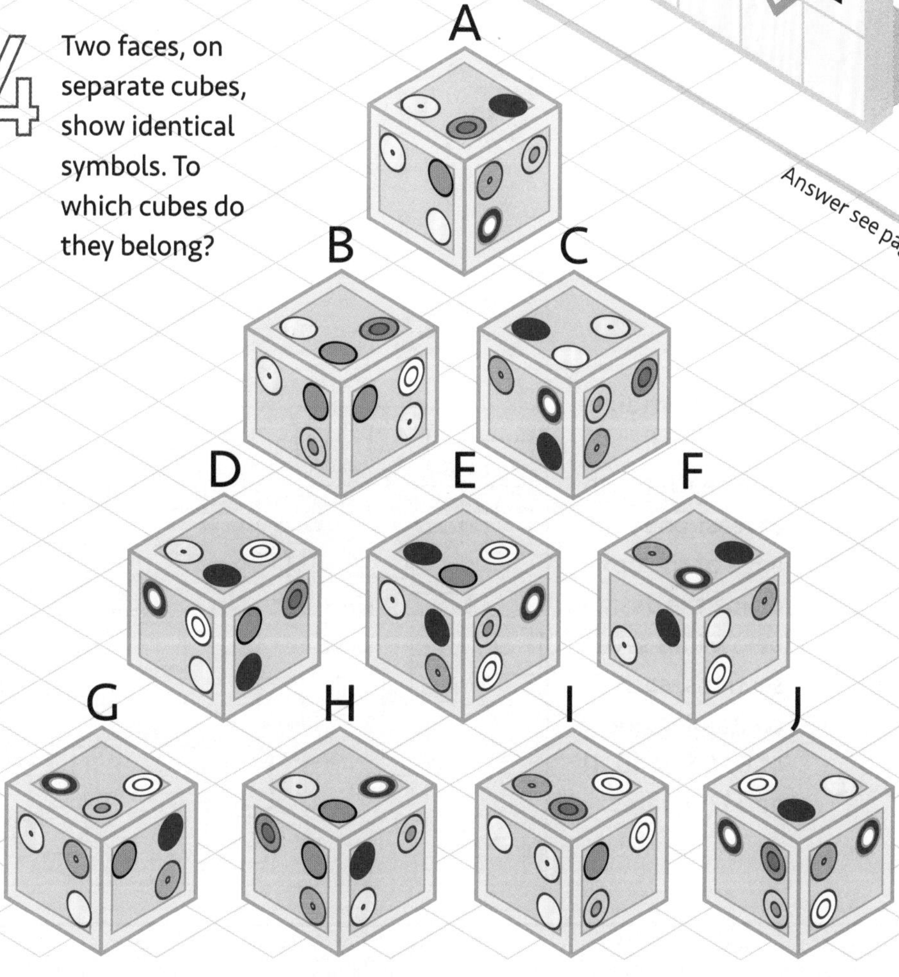

Answer see page 141

155

The grid below shows the numbers on a full set of dominoes, from 0-0 to 9-9 inclusive, that have been pushed together horizontally and vertically to make a solid rectangle. Complete the grid to show where each domino lies.

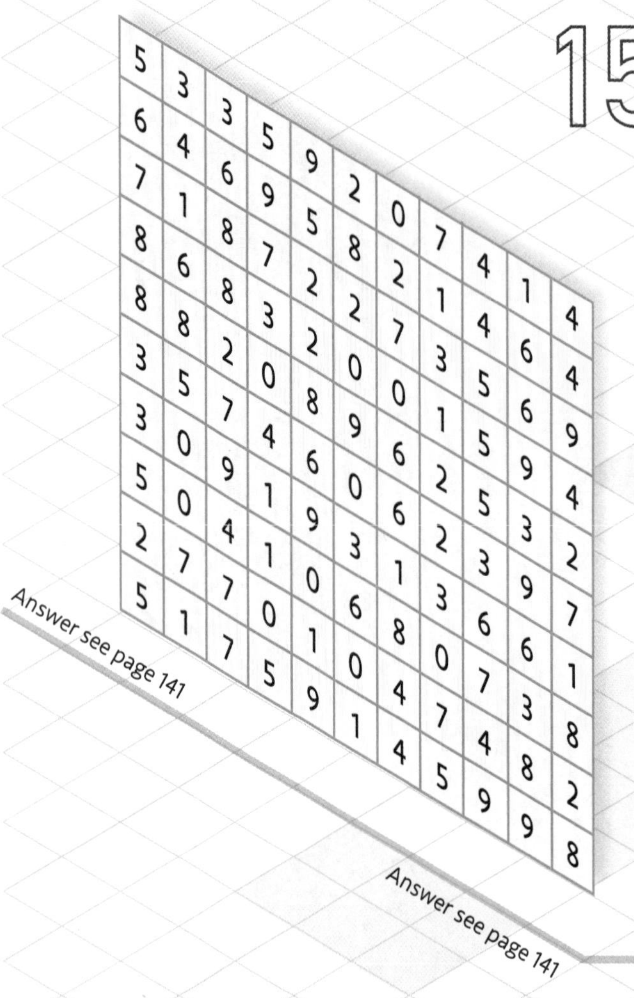

5	3	3	5	9	2	0	7	4	1	4
6	4	6	9	5	8	2	1	4	6	4
7	1	8	7	2	2	7	3	5	6	9
8	6	8	3	2	0	0	1	5	9	4
8	8	2	0	8	9	6	2	5	3	2
3	5	7	4	6	0	6	2	3	9	7
3	0	9	1	9	3	1	3	6	6	1
5	0	4	1	0	6	8	0	7	3	8
2	7	7	0	1	0	4	7	4	8	2
5	1	7	5	9	1	4	5	9	9	8

Answer see page 141

Answer see page 141

156

Using six straight lines, which must each touch at least one edge of the box, divide the design below into seven sections, each containing one of 6, 7, 8, 9, 10, 11 and 12 squares.

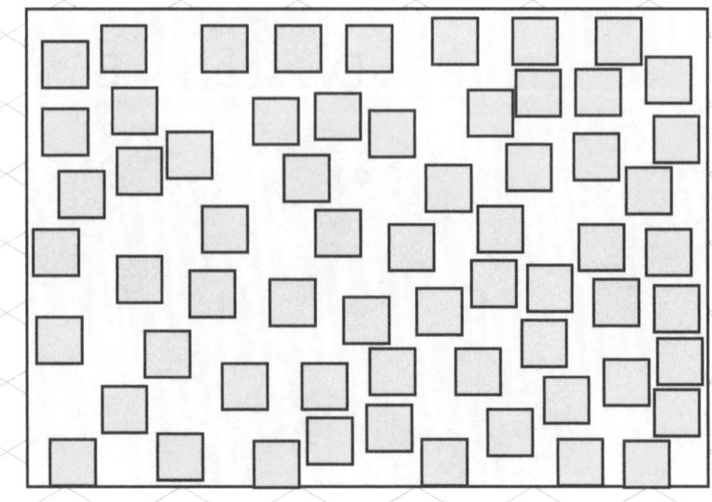

157

Complete the grid below so that each unbroken horizontal and vertical stretch of light cells sums to the total indicated in the cell to the left or above the stretch respectively. Each cell may contain only the digits 1 – 9, and no digit may be repeated in any given stretch of cells.

Answer see page 141

From the information below, where did the angler who used a jig lure in the competition come from?

The rancher, whose name was Sarah, finished immediately above the secretary. The angler from Tulsa worked as a singer, whilst the angler from Chicago used a spoon lure, and the angler from Portland was named Julie. The angler with a Toyota used a spinnerbait lure. The angler who worked as a taxi driver drove a Lexus, whilst the third-placed angler was named Laura. The resident of Derry was the first-placed angler. The angler with a Ford placed adjacent to the angler who used worms, whilst the angler with the Lexus placed adjacent to the angler who used a crankbait lure. The angler named Steven drove a Tesla, but the angler from Albuquerque drove a Chevrolet. The angler from Derry placed adjacent to the angler who worked as a manager. The angler named Mark placed adjacent to the angler with a Ford.

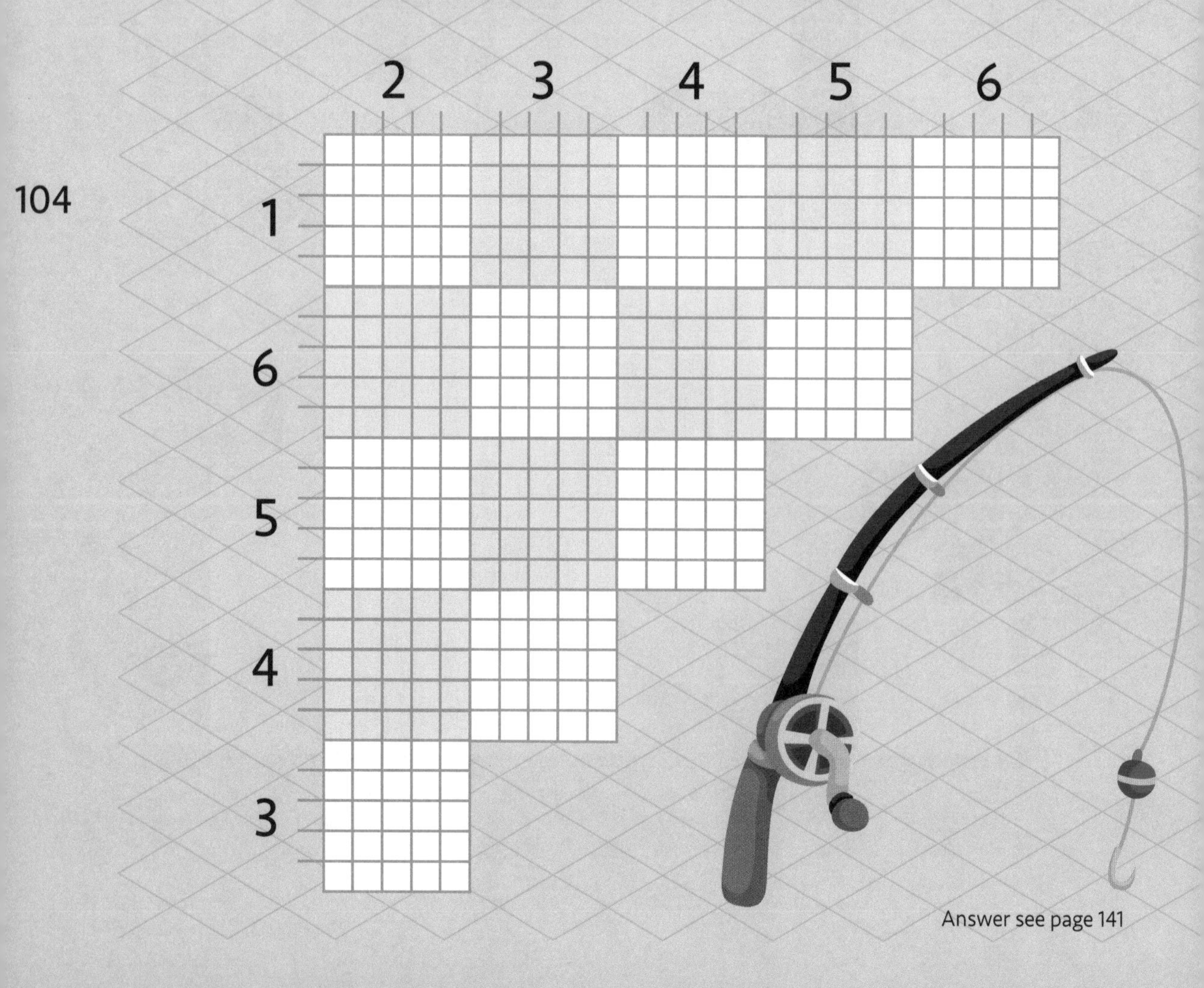

Answer see page 141

159

The pieces can be assembled into a shape. What is it?

Answer see page 141

Answer see page 141

160

In each square, the arrow shows the direction you must move in. The numbers in some squares show that square's position in the correct sequence of moves. Move from top left to bottom right, visiting each square in the grid exactly once.

1

16

161

What number should replace the question mark?

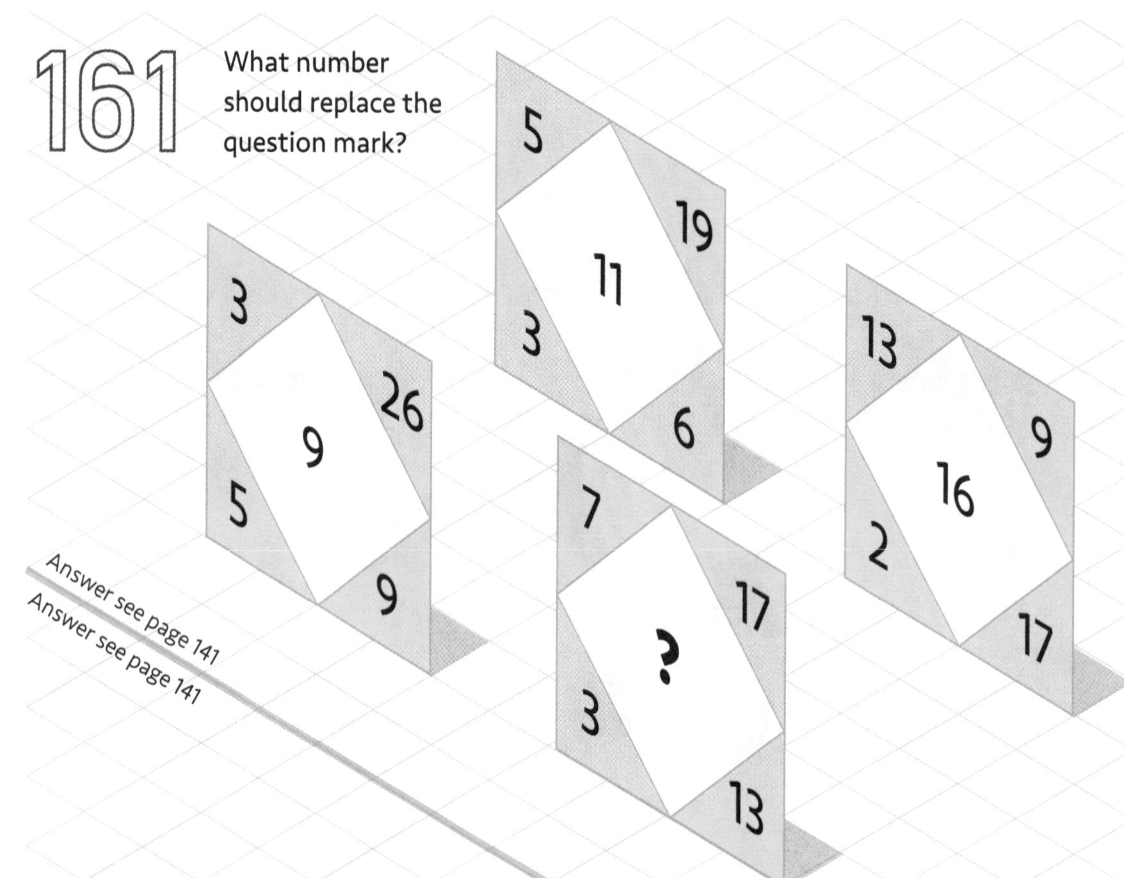

Answer see page 141
Answer see page 141

Are the following statements true or false?

i. Ion Iliescu is a former president of Romania.
ii. Krypton is green.
iii. The game of Liar's Dice originated in north Africa.
iv. Nether Wallop is a village in England.
v. Permutable prime numbers can only include the digits 3, 7, and 9.
vi. Pink carnations are said to represent motherly love.
vii. Portland is the capital of Oregon.
viii. Salamanders generally lay their eggs in the water.
ix. The constellation of Vela represents a herdsman.
x. The telescope was invented in the Netherlands in the 17th century.

Assemble the pieces shown below into a square grid which reads the same across as it does downwards.

3
6
2

6
3
4

7 8 1

3 2 5

1 3
7 2

2 4 5

3 4 5

5 1
2
4

5 8 1

2 1 4

5 4
1

2
5
8

3 0
0 1

8 2 3
3

7
2 1

Answer see page 141

164

Decipher the names of several celebrities using the telephone dial as a guide.

585427623787
783832872364
8666953356637
7224356223267
2782377746478336
5225432426

Answer see page 141

165

Complete the grid below so that each number shown forms part of a group of horizontally and/or vertically connected cells. The number of cells in the group must be the same as the number shown on the grid. So a '2' indicates a group that is a pair of two cells. No group shares a horizontal or vertical boundary with another group of the same size/number. Every group of cells has at least one number shown.

	4	2	3						2
			8		4	4			8
	2	8				7	7	8	
			8	5				7	
	2	9				7		9	
4	4							8	
6								7	
		5	5	3	7			2	4
4	4		5		2				
				2					5

Answer see page 141

Answer see page 141

Using seven straight lines, divide the design below into eleven sections, each containing precisely twelve circles of at least two different shades.

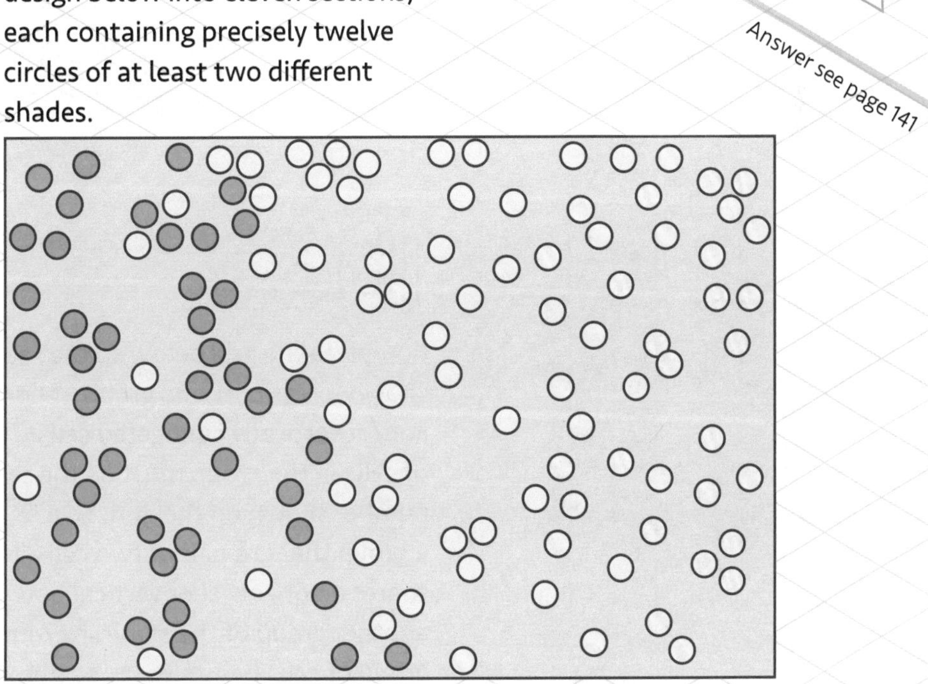

In each square, the arrow shows the direction you must move in. The numbers in some squares show that square's position in the correct sequence of moves. Move from top left to bottom right, visiting each square in the grid exactly once.

1

16

Answer see page 141

168

Complete the grid below so that each number shown forms part of a group of horizontally and/or vertically connected cells. The number of cells in the group must be the same as the number shown on the grid. So a '2' indicates a group that is a pair of two cells. No group shares a horizontal or vertical boundary with another group of the same size/number. Every group of cells has at least one number shown.

Answer see page 141

169

Ten vessels are hidden in the grid below, four one cell ships, three two-cell ships, two three-cell ships, and one four-cell ship. Ships are positioned horizontally or vertically. No two ships are immediately adjacent to each other, including diagonally. The numbers next to each row and column show the total number of ship segments in that line. Identify the exact locations of all ten vessels. Some ship segments and/or spaces of empty ocean are shown to assist you.

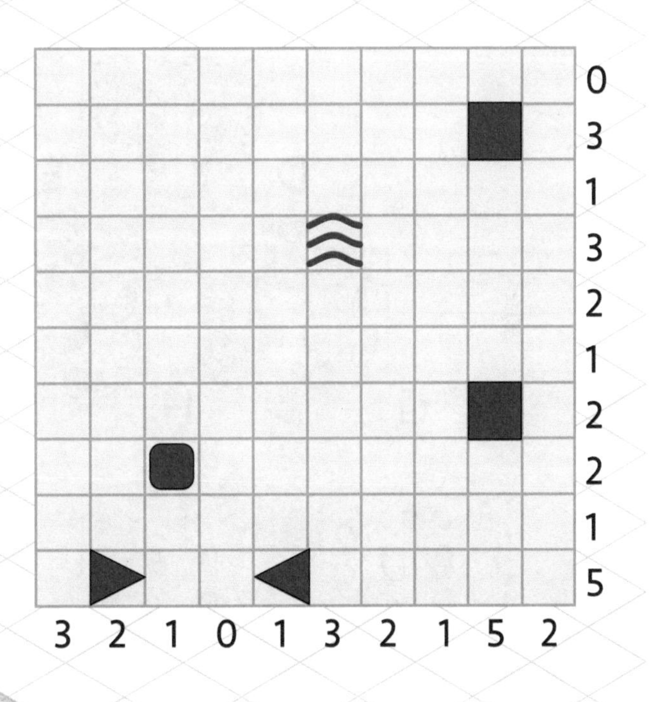

170

Adeline likes A. A. Milne but not Beatrix Potter. Rudolph likes Virginia Woolf but not P. G. Wodehouse. Hakim likes J. R. R. Tolkien but not Henry James. Which of the following does Byron like?

JANE AUSTEN

WILLIAM GOLDING

JOANNE HARRIS

LEWIS CARROLL

Answer see page 142

171

Two faces, on separate cubes, show identical symbols. To which cubes do they belong?

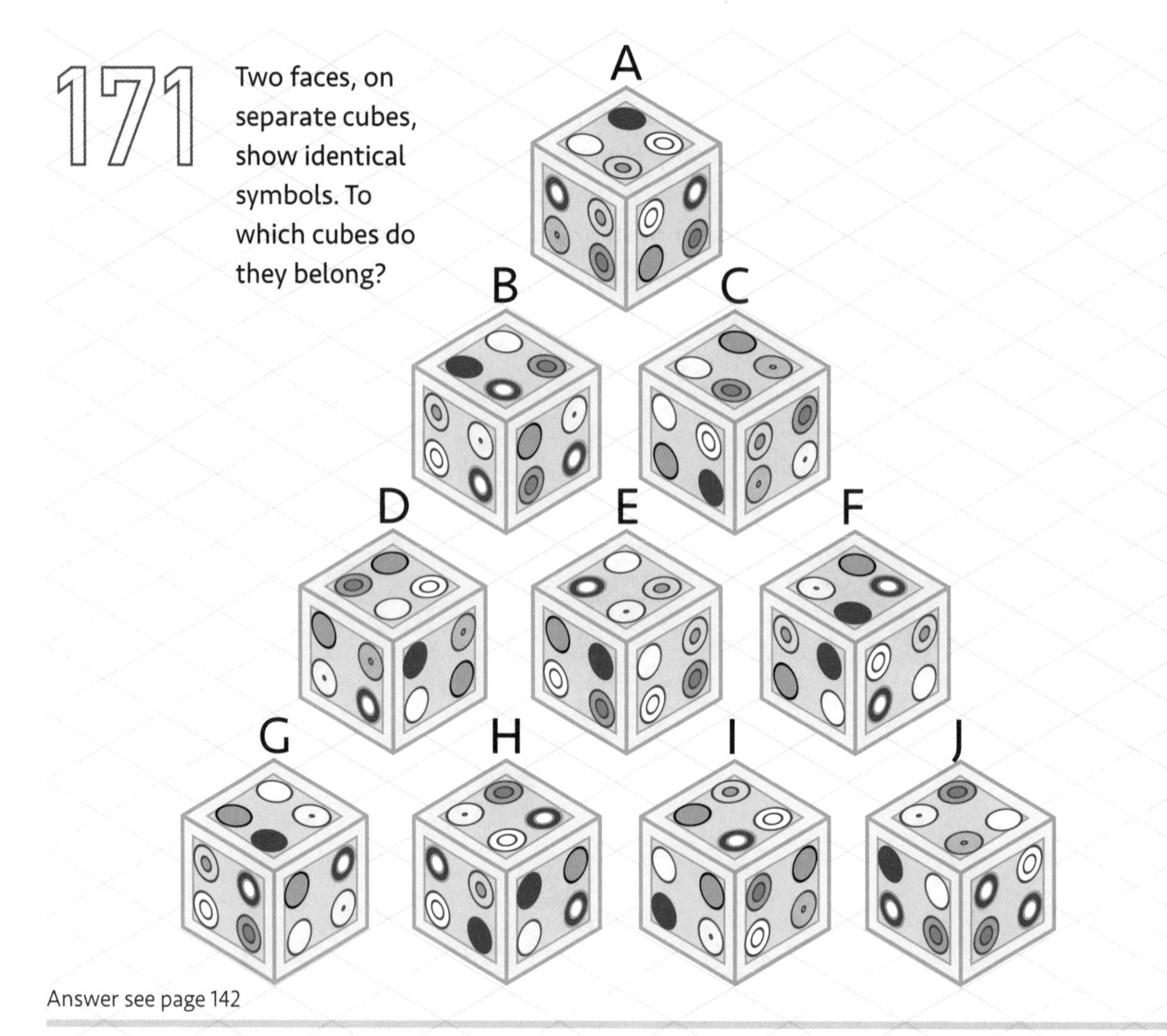

Answer see page 142

Answer see page 142

172

The pieces can be assembled into a regular geometric shape. What is it?

173

From the information below, where does Anthony live?

1. Shannon lives in Essex. Her favourite puzzle is neither Wordsearch nor Kakuro.
2. The Cornwall puzzler is a police officer, and is not the Crossword fan, who is named Christine.
3. The driver lives in Hampshire.
4. The maze fan is called Charles, and he is not a carpenter.
5. The programmer is not in love with either Sudoku or mazes, and does not live in Derbyshire.
6. Anthony does not live in Edinburgh.
7. The Wordsearch fan is an analyst, and is not called Tammy.
9. One puzzler lives in Derbyshire.

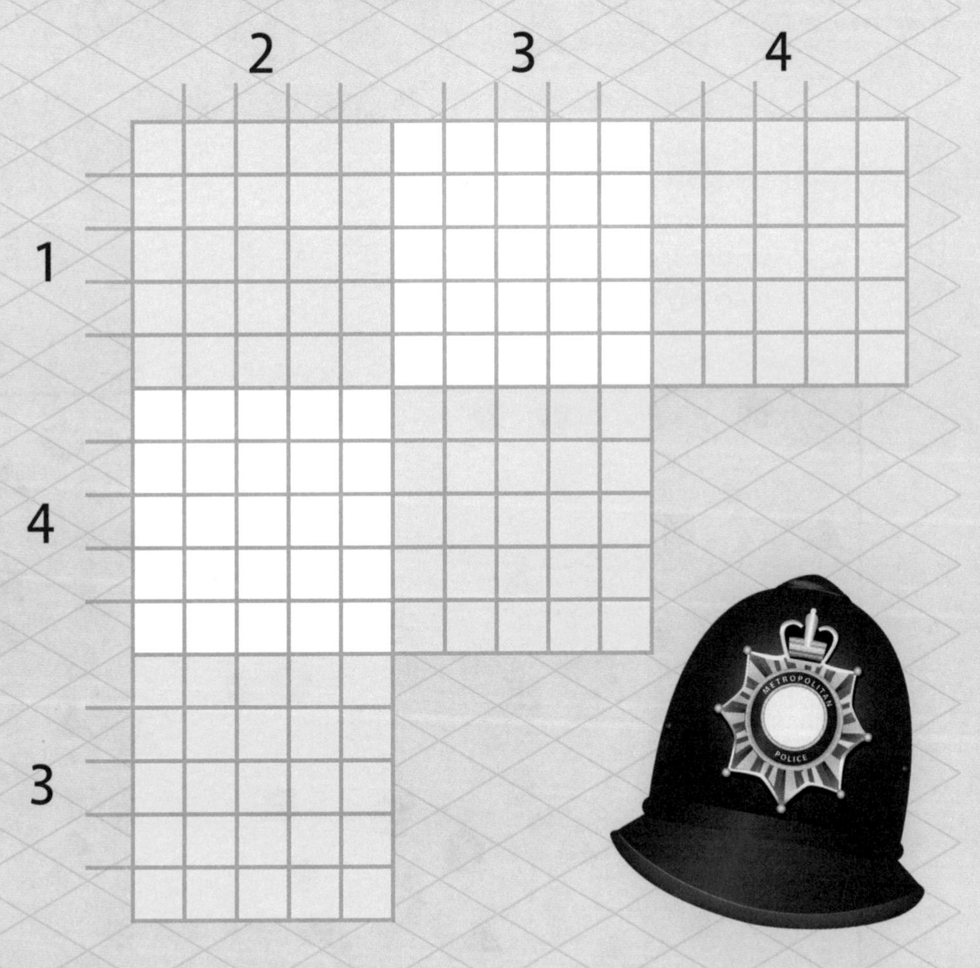

Answer see page 142

Connect each pair of identical numbers with a single continuous path running horizontally and/or vertically through the cells of the grid below. Paths may switch direction at the centre of a cell, but may not branch, loop back on themselves, or cross. When the grid is complete, each cell will contain a single path section.

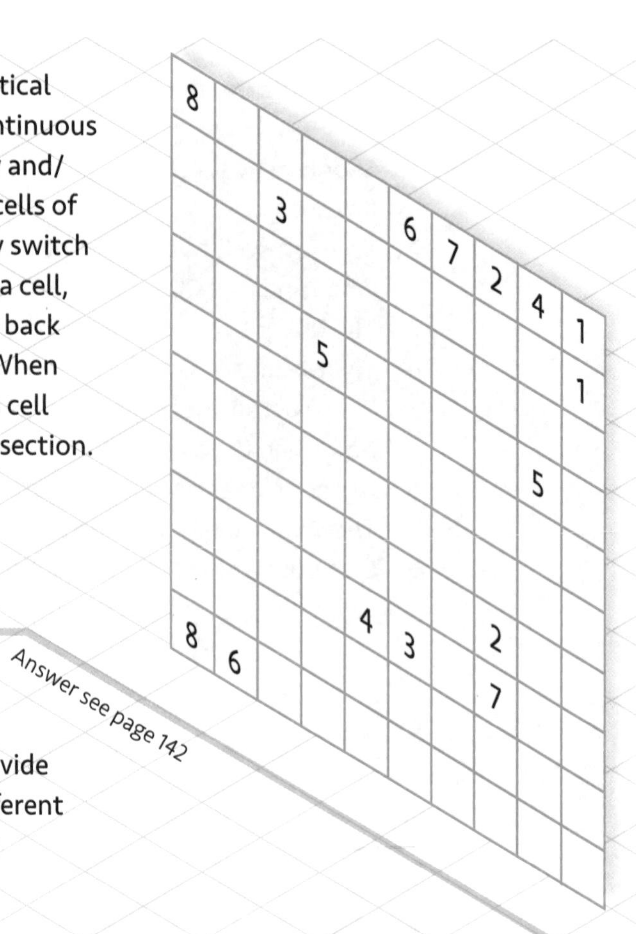

Answer see page 142

Using six straight lines, divide the design below into different sections, each containing precisely three circles.

Answer see page 142

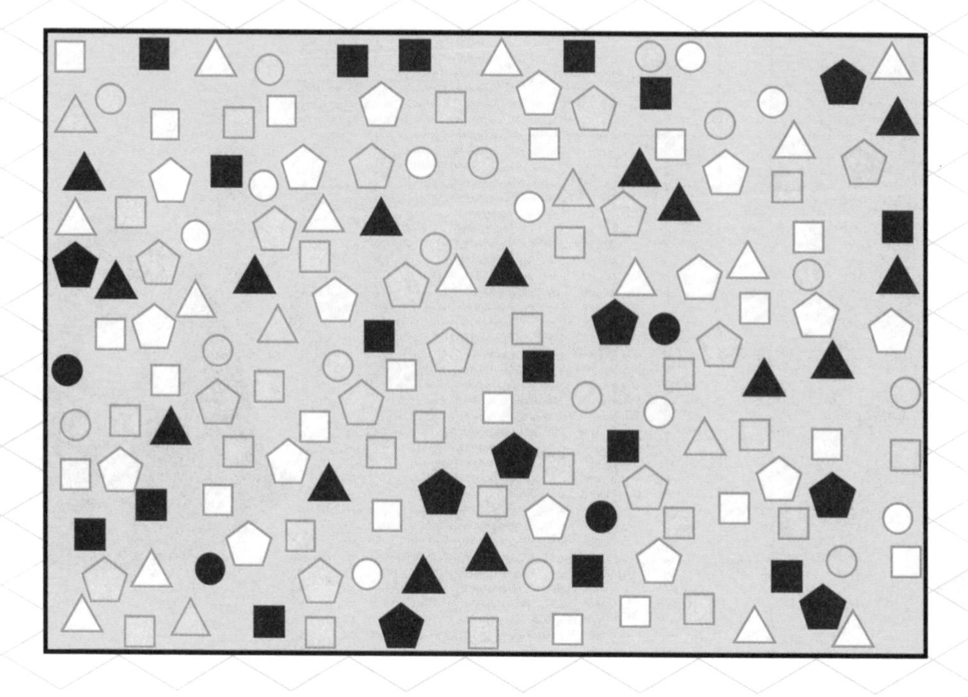

176

Which of the four pieces A to D fits to complete the shape?

A

B

C

D

Answer see page 142

Answer see page 142

177

Complete the grid below so that each number shown forms part of a group of horizontally and/or vertically connected cells. The number of cells in the group must be the same as the number shown on the grid. So a '2' indicates a group that is a pair of two cells. No group shares a horizontal or vertical boundary with another group of the same size/number. Every group of cells has at least one number shown.

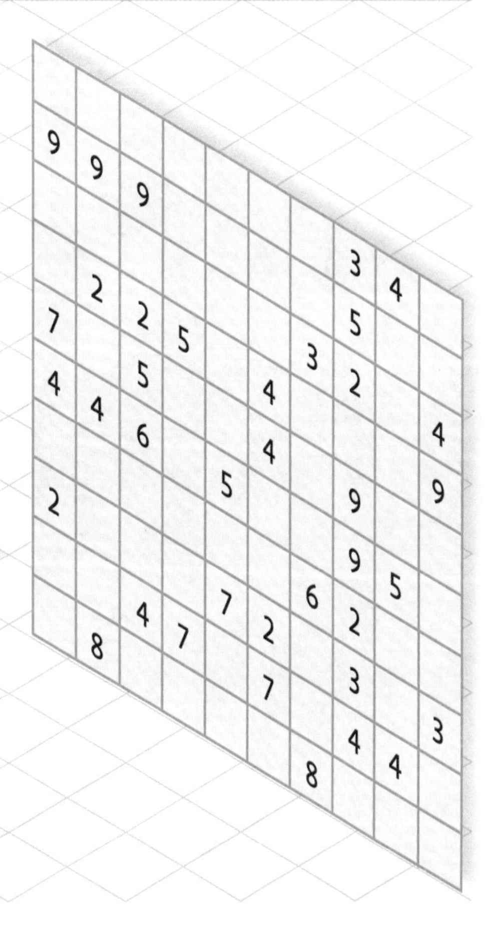

Decipher the names of several celebrities using the telephone dial as a guide.

8443796637

253248466377

527667828426

24747436796784

762378336476

536643372647866

Answer see page 142

179

Shade the cells in the grid below so that each row and column holds continuous lines of shaded cells of the lengths indicated by the numbers shown at the start of that row or column. Blocks are separated from others in the same row or column by at least one empty cell. A picture will emerge when the cells are shaded correctly.

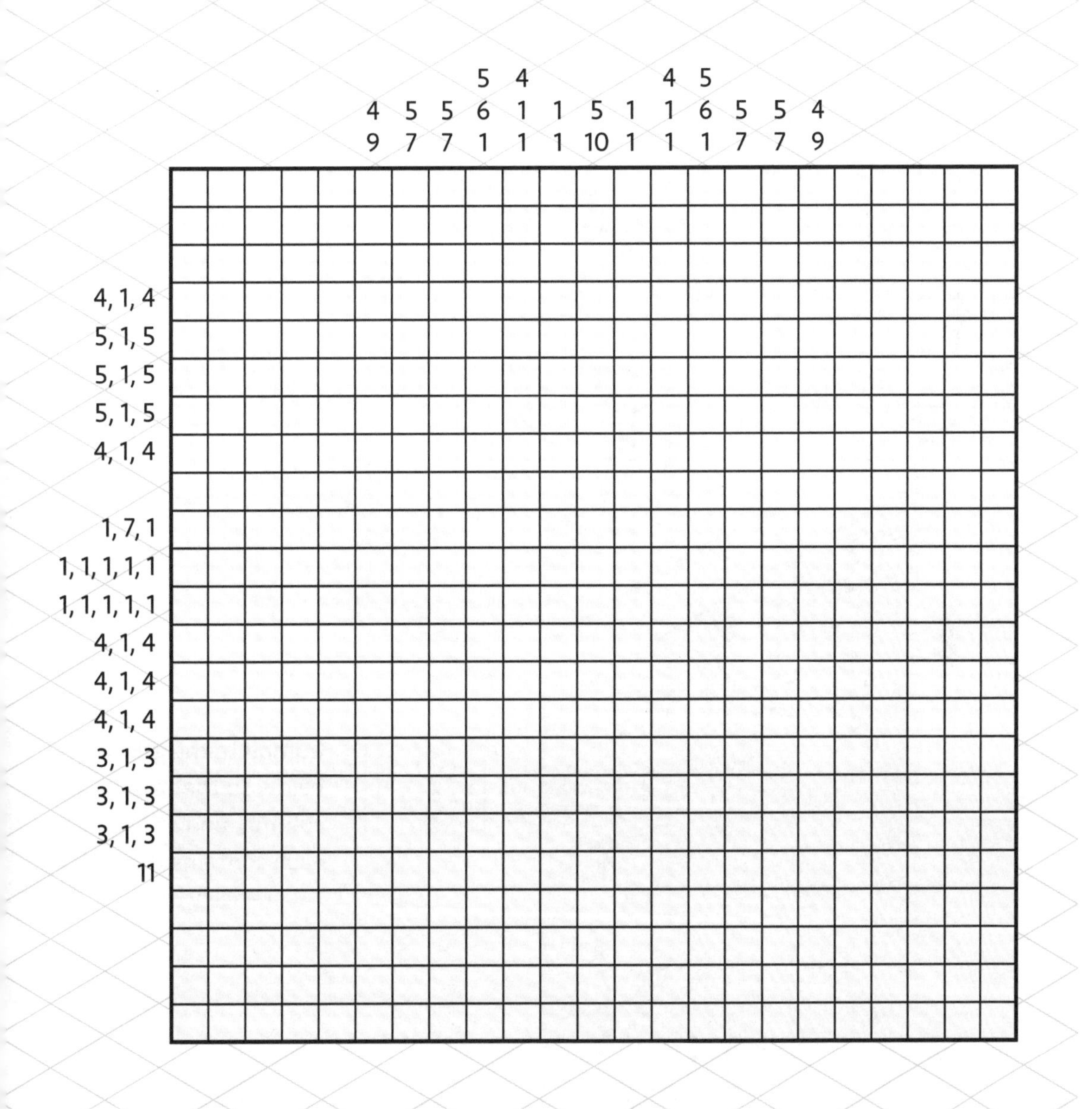

Answer see page 142

180

In each square, the arrow shows the direction you must move in. The numbers in some squares show that square's position in the correct sequence of moves. Move from top left to bottom right, visiting each square in the grid exactly once.

Answer see page 142

181

Complete the grid below so that every row, column, and 3x3 square each contains the digits 1-9 precisely once.

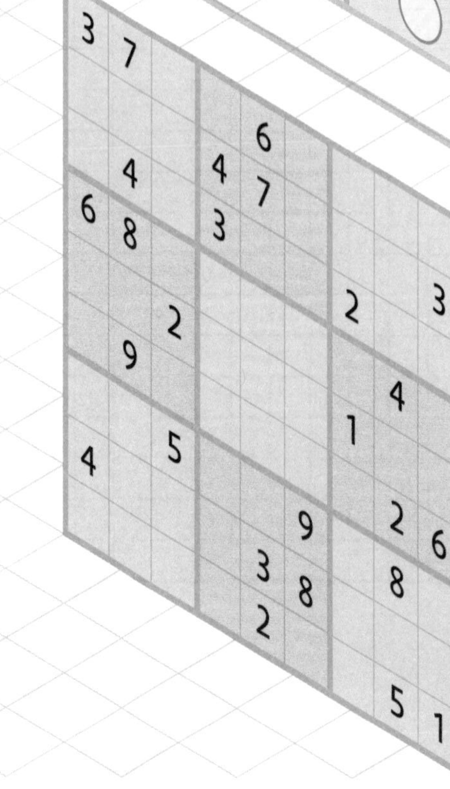

Answer see page 142

182

What number should replace the question mark?

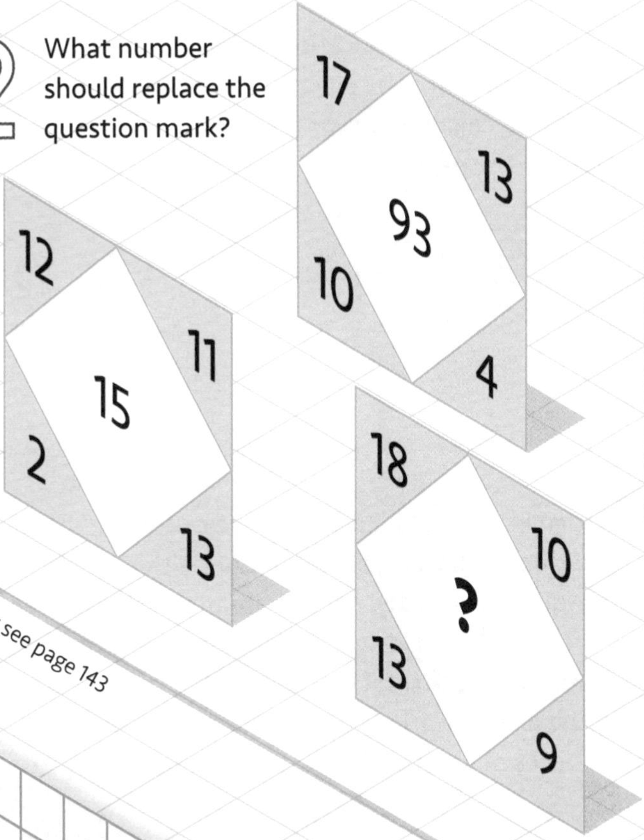

Answer see page 143

Answer see page 142

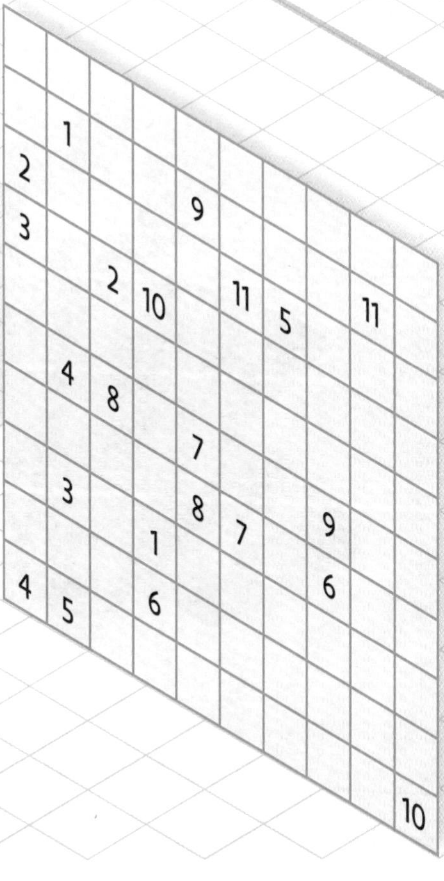

183

Connect each pair of identical numbers with a single continuous path running horizontally and/or vertically through the cells of the grid below. Paths may switch direction at the centre of a cell, but may not branch, loop back on themselves, or cross. When the grid is complete, each cell will contain a single path section.

Fill in missing plus, minus, multiplication, division, and/or factorial signs to make the equation below correct, performing all calculations strictly in the order they appear on the page.

Answer see page 143

Ten vessels are hidden in the grid below, four one cell ships, three two-cell ships, two three-cell ships, and one four-cell ship. Ships are positioned horizontally or vertically. No two ships are immediately adjacent to each other, including diagonally. The numbers next to each row and column show the total number of ship segments in that line. Identify the exact locations of all ten vessels. Some ship segments and/or spaces of empty ocean are shown to assist you.

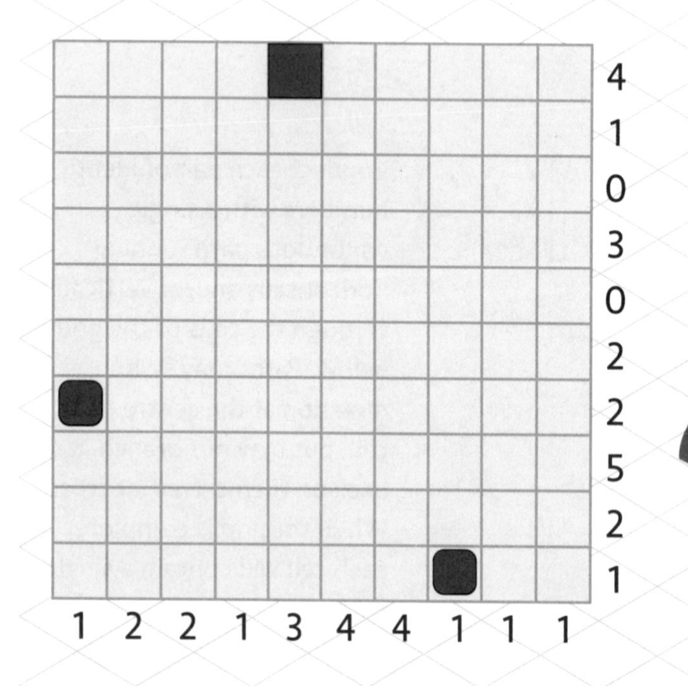

Answer see page 143

In the grid below, how much is each symbol worth?

68

81

71

77

68

Answer see page 143

Answer see page 143

187

Fill in missing plus, minus, multiplication, division, and/or factorial signs to make the equation below correct, performing all calculations strictly in the order they appear on the page.

5 16 20 3 25 11 2 25 8 = 944

Shade the cells in the grid below so that each row and column holds continuous lines of shaded cells of the lengths indicated by the numbers shown at the start of that row or column. Blocks are separated from others in the same row or column by at least one empty cell. A picture will emerge when the cells are shaded correctly.

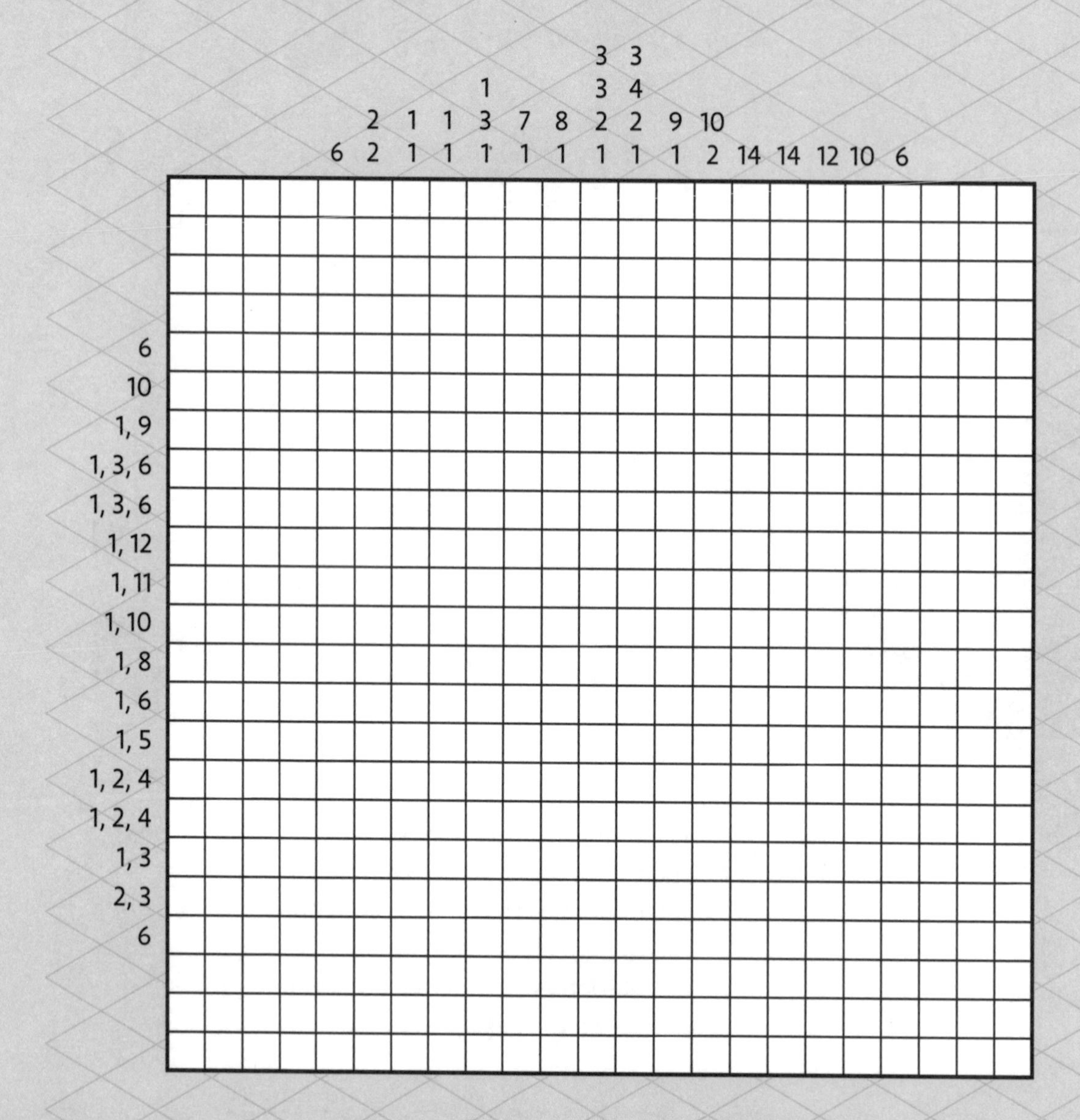

Answer see page 143

Complete the grid below so that each number shown forms part of a group of horizontally and/or vertically connected cells. The number of cells in the group must be the same as the number shown on the grid. So a '2' indicates a group that is a pair of two cells. No group shares a horizontal or vertical boundary with another group of the same size/number. Every group of cells has at least one number shown.

Answer see page 143

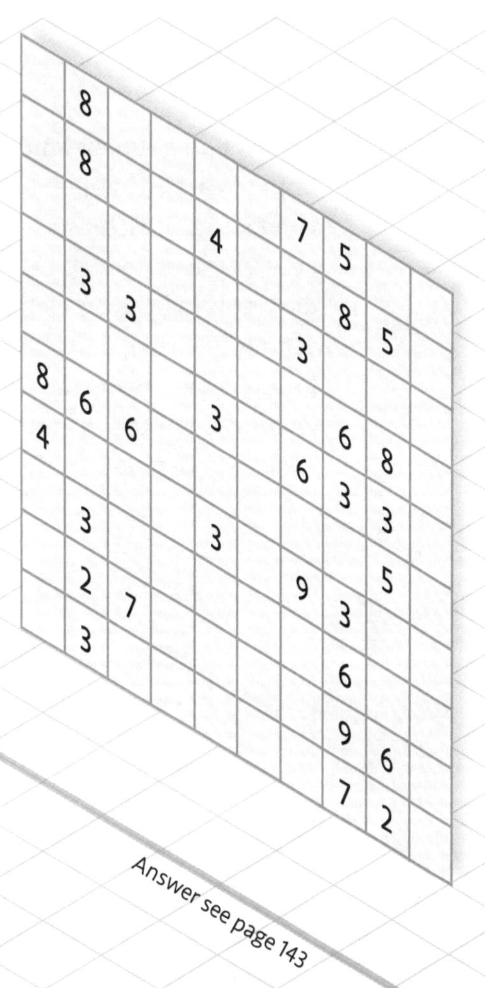

Answer see page 143

190

In each square, the arrow shows the direction you must move in. The numbers in some squares show that square's position in the correct sequence of moves. Move from top left to bottom right, visiting each square in the grid exactly once.

191

From the information below, which person had a sausage sandwich?

Jeremy had a turkey sandwich, but was not at the cat show to look at Bobtail cats – that person was wearing a red sweater. The person with a cheddar sandwich was wearing a blue sweater, and was not there to look at Siamese or Persian cats. One person was wearing a green sweater. Tanya did not bring the omelette sandwich. Joshua did not bring the omelette sandwich either, and wasn't there to look at Bobtail cats. The person who'd brought a brie sandwich was there to look at Shorthair cats, and was not wearing a white sweater. Lucy was there to investigate Manx cats. Ryan, was wearing a mauve sweater, and was not there to look at Shorthair cats.

2 3 4

1

4

3

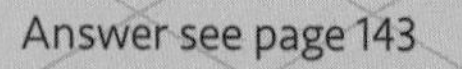
Answer see page 143

Decipher the names of several celebrities using the telephone dial as a guide.

53774222522
53846772239
2546832789663
3739227796673
7692628546766
52839467538

Answer see page 143

Complete the grid below so that each unbroken horizontal and vertical stretch of light cells sums to the total indicated in the cell to the left or above the stretch respectively. Each cell may contain only the digits 1 – 9, and no digit may be repeated in any given stretch of cells.

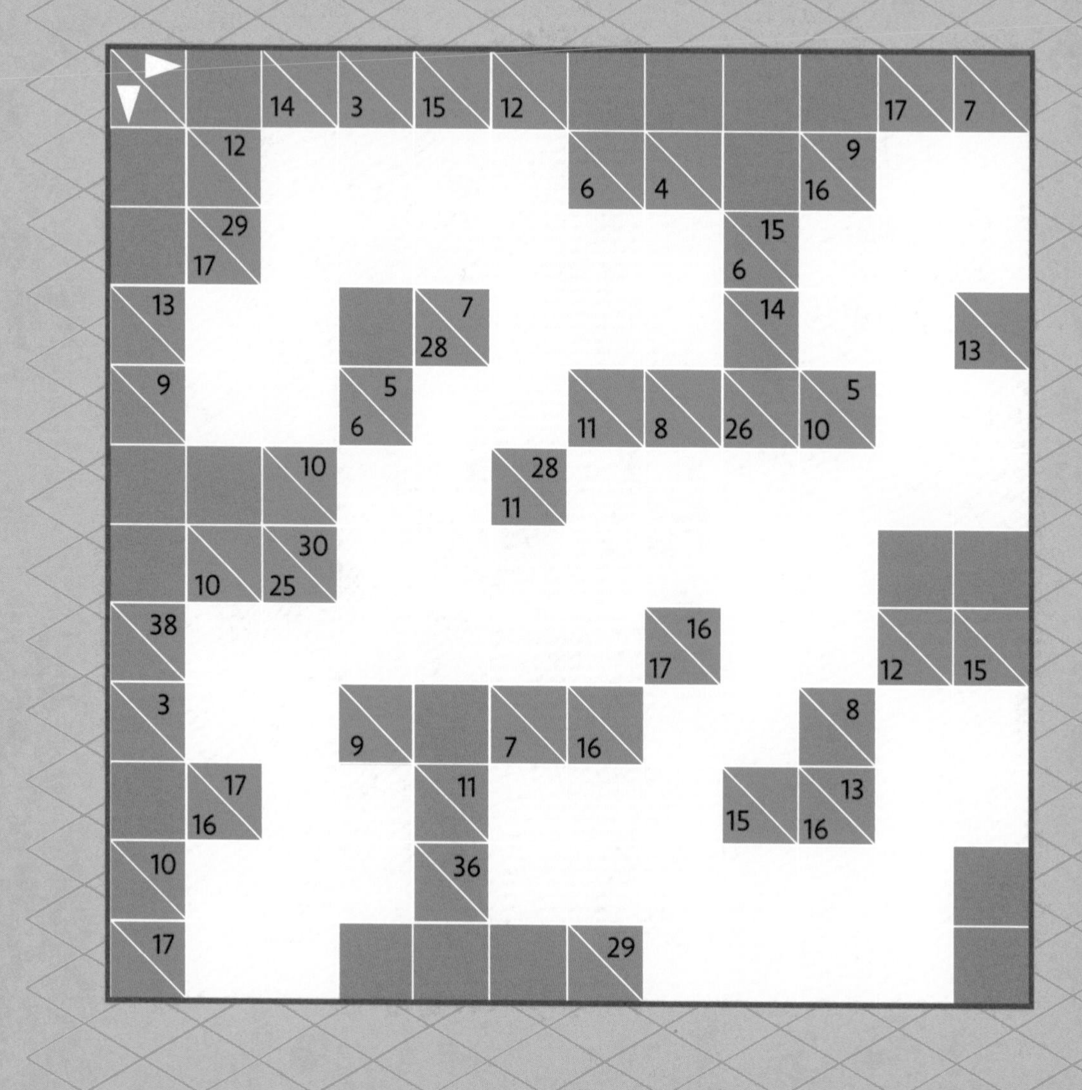

Answer see page 143

In the grid below, how much is each symbol worth?

25

33

26

34

32

31

Answer see page 143

		8	3				9	
1					5			
	6			4			5	
			5			8		3
	8		4		9		7	
3		2			8			
	2			5			4	
			9					6
	4					5		

Answer see page 143

195

Complete the grid below so that every row, column, and 3x3 square each contains the digits 1-9 precisely once.

From the information below, where did the person who wanted to adopt a terrier come from?

The person from Hampshire was the first of the five to be interviewed at the centre. Kenneth had grey hair. The person from Norfolk worked as a chef. Tina was interviewed immediately before or after a person with blonde hair. The person from Strathclyde wanted to adopt a corgi. The professor, whose name was Gregory, had his interview immediately before the marketer. The person with red hair wanted to adopt a spaniel. The writer had black hair, whilst Lori had the middle interview spot. The person with blonde hair was interviewed immediately before or after the person who wanted to adopt a labrador. Patricia was from Powys. The person with black hair was interviewed immediately before or after the person wanted to adopt a poodle. The person from Cumbria had brown hair. The person from Hampshire was interviewed immediately before or after the person who worked as a optician.

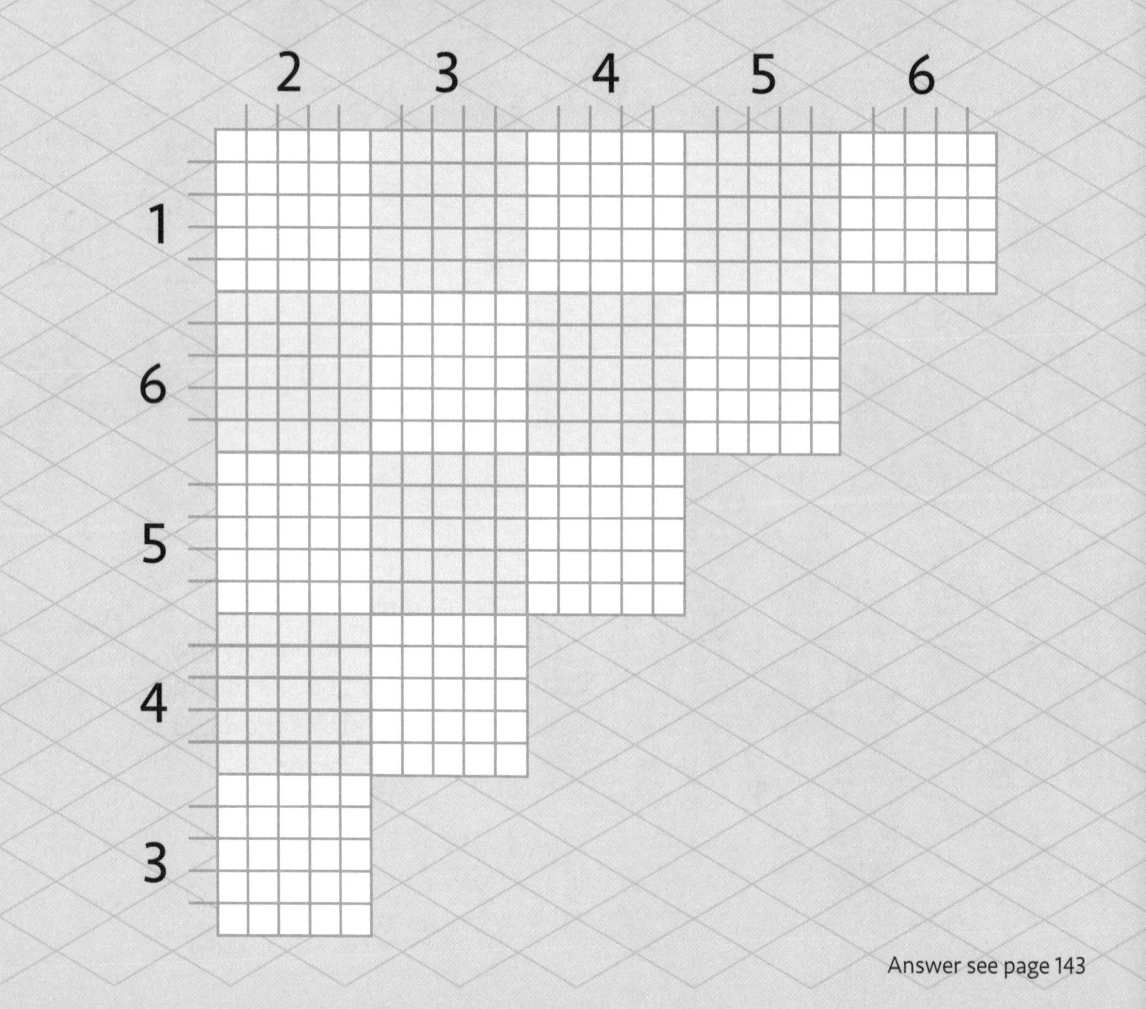

Answer see page 143

197

Complete the grid below so that every row, column, and 3x3 square each contains the digits 1-9 precisely once. The sum of the digits in each group of cells with a dotted outline must total the number in the group's top/left corner.

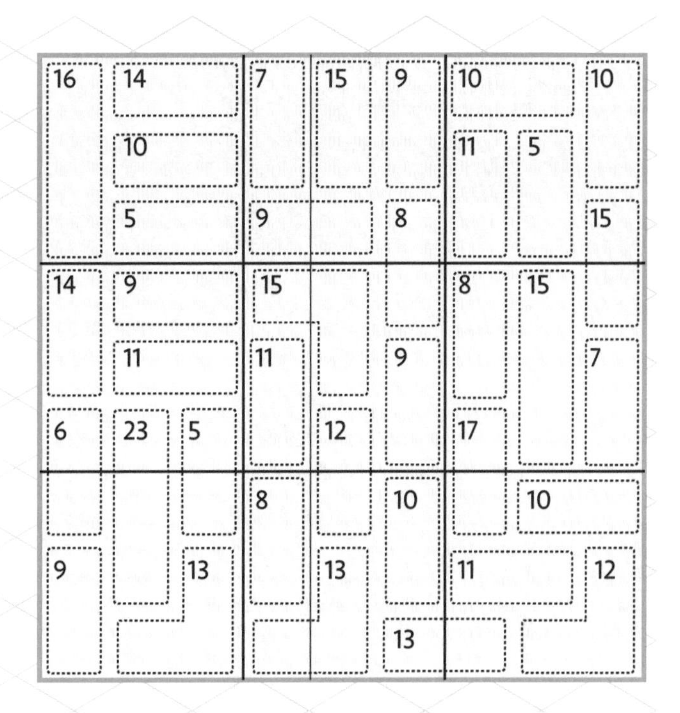

Answer see page 144

198

What number should replace the question mark?

Answer see page 144

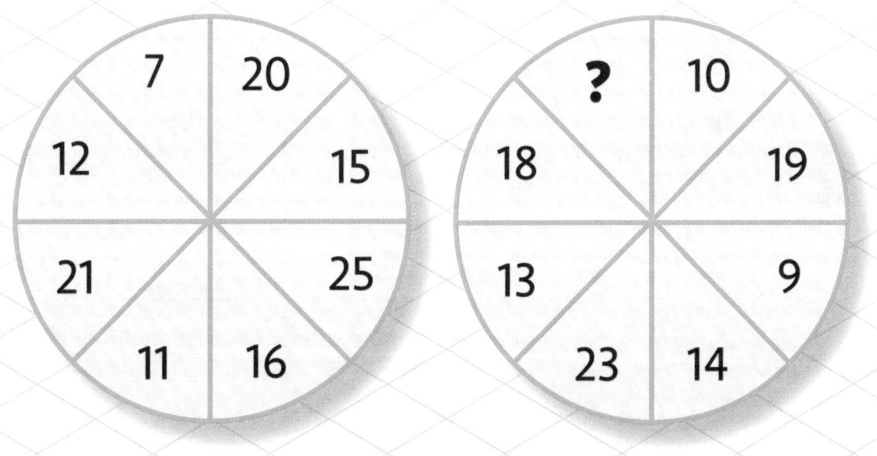

Answer see page 144

199

Patrick Armstrong likes Aston Martin but not Jaguar. Cyndi Stone likes Land Rover but not Rolls Royce. Morag MacDonald likes Bentley but not Lotus. Which of the following does Harding Tooley like?

ASCARI RANGE ROVER BRISTOL MINI

Which symbols are missing from the grid below?

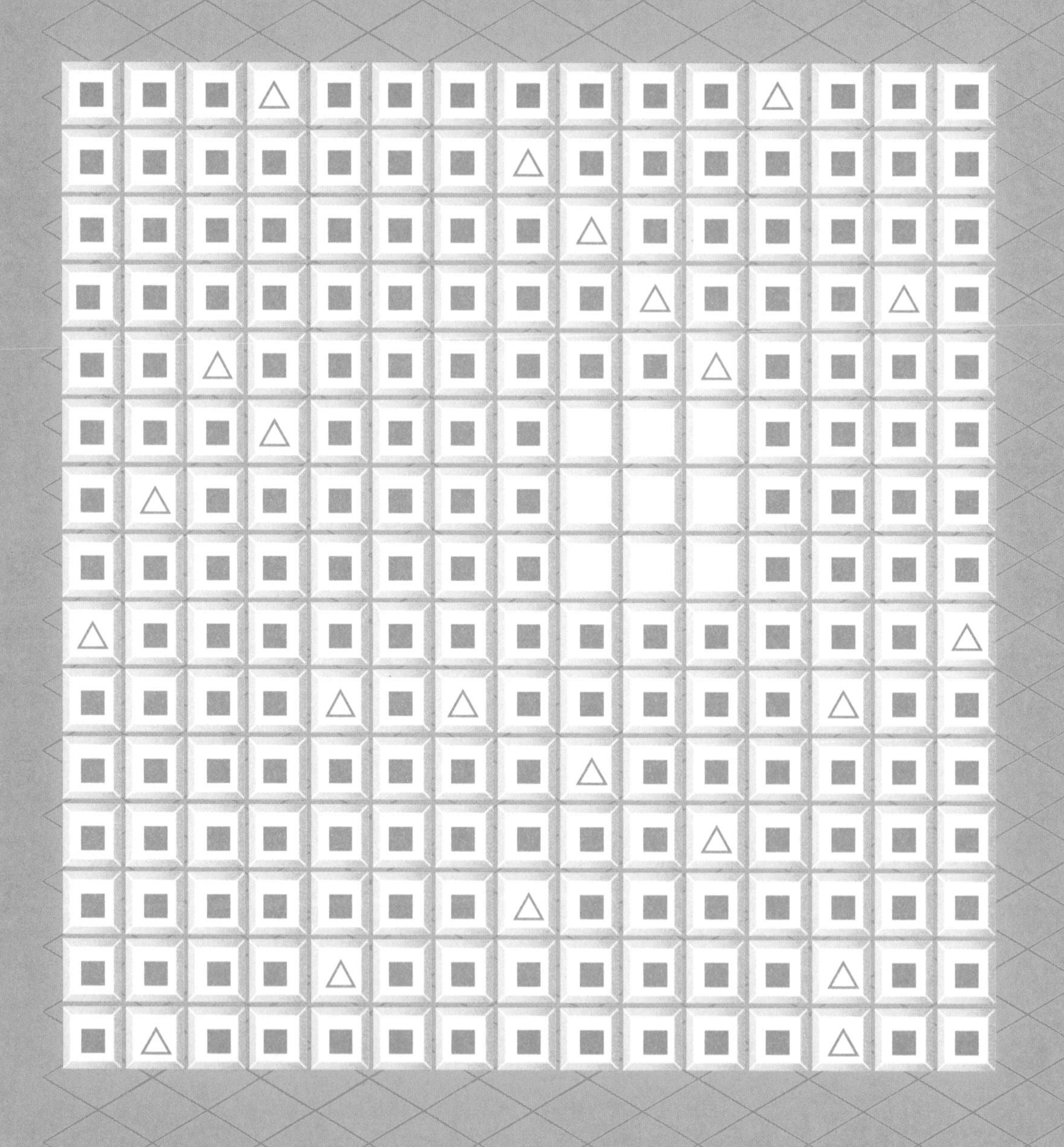

Answer see page 144

THE ANSWERS

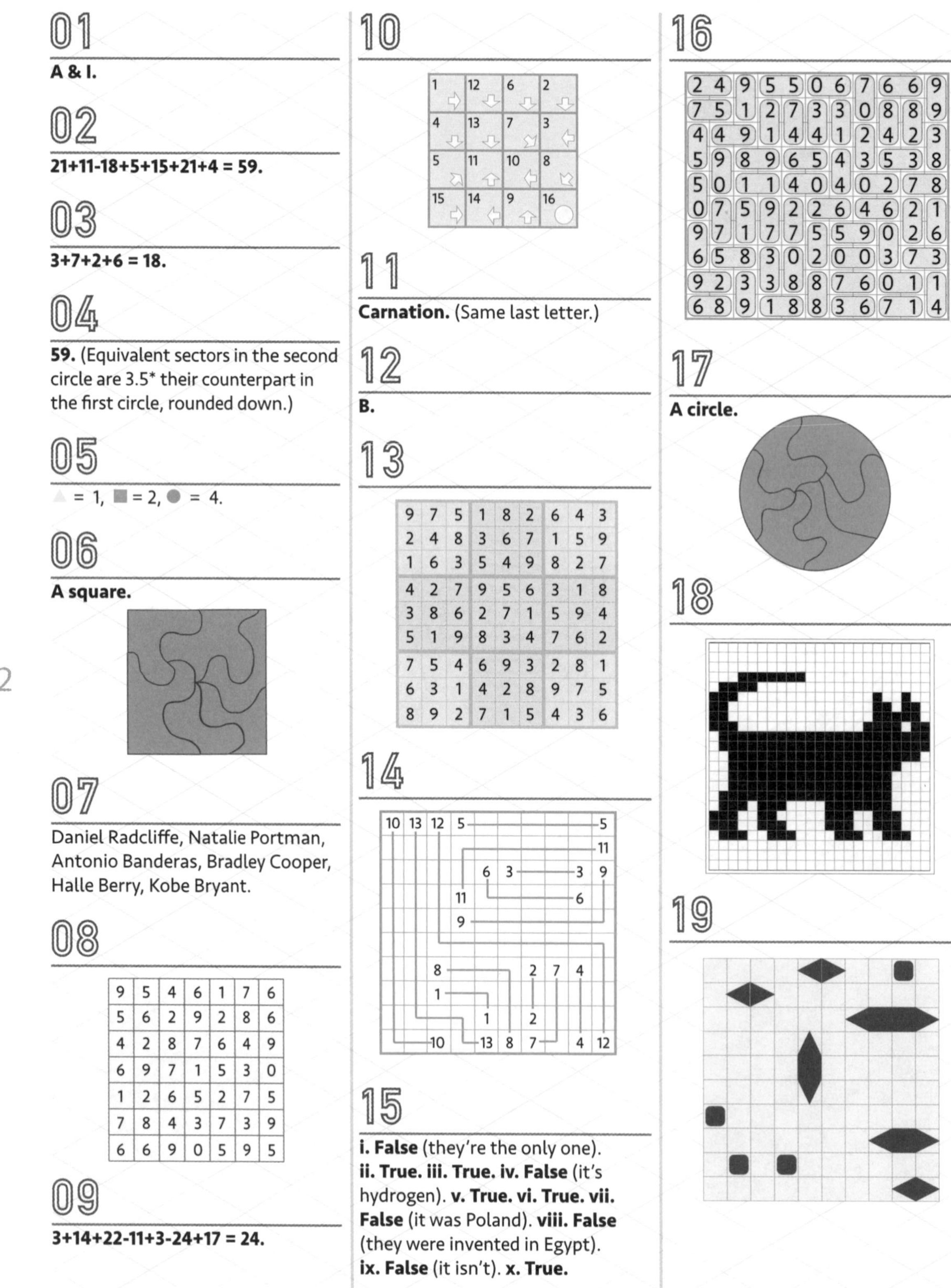

01

A & I.

02

21+11-18+5+15+21+4 = 59.

03

3+7+2+6 = 18.

04

59. (Equivalent sectors in the second circle are 3.5* their counterpart in the first circle, rounded down.)

05

▲ = 1, ■ = 2, ● = 4.

06

A square.

07

Daniel Radcliffe, Natalie Portman, Antonio Banderas, Bradley Cooper, Halle Berry, Kobe Bryant.

08

9	5	4	6	1	7	6
5	6	2	9	2	8	6
4	2	8	7	6	4	9
6	9	7	1	5	3	0
1	2	6	5	2	7	5
7	8	4	3	7	3	9
6	6	9	0	5	9	5

09

3+14+22-11+3-24+17 = 24.

10

1	12	6	2
4	13	7	3
5	11	10	8
15	14	9	16

11

Carnation. (Same last letter.)

12

B.

13

9	7	5	1	8	2	6	4	3
2	4	8	3	6	7	1	5	9
1	6	3	5	4	9	8	2	7
4	2	7	9	5	6	3	1	8
3	8	6	2	7	1	5	9	4
5	1	9	8	3	4	7	6	2
7	5	4	6	9	3	2	8	1
6	3	1	4	2	8	9	7	5
8	9	2	7	1	5	4	3	6

14

15

i. False (they're the only one). **ii. True. iii. True. iv. False** (it's hydrogen). **v. True. vi. True. vii. False** (it was Poland). **viii. False** (they were invented in Egypt). **ix. False** (it isn't). **x. True.**

16

2	4	9	5	5	0	6	7	6	6	9
7	5	1	2	7	3	3	0	8	8	9
4	4	9	1	4	4	1	2	4	2	3
5	9	8	9	6	5	4	3	5	3	8
5	0	1	1	4	0	4	0	2	7	8
0	7	5	9	2	2	6	4	6	2	1
9	7	1	7	7	5	5	9	0	2	6
6	5	8	3	0	2	0	0	3	7	3
9	2	3	3	8	8	7	6	0	1	1
6	8	9	1	8	8	3	6	7	1	4

17

A circle.

18

19

20

2	3	1	6	4	5
1	5	6	4	3	2
4	1	3	5	2	6
5	2	4	3	6	1
6	4	2	1	5	3
3	6	5	2	1	4

21

21. (Equivalent sectors in both circles sum to a total of 35.)

22

Michel.

Georges, a blacksmith from Bagnol, liked wines from Champagne. **Iva**, a whitesmith from Rouen, liked wines from Burgundy. **Jacques**, a greensmith from Aix, liked wines from Beaujolais. **Michel**, a goldsmith from Reims, liked wines from Bordeaux. **Veronique**, a tinsmith from Paris, liked wines from Alsace.

23

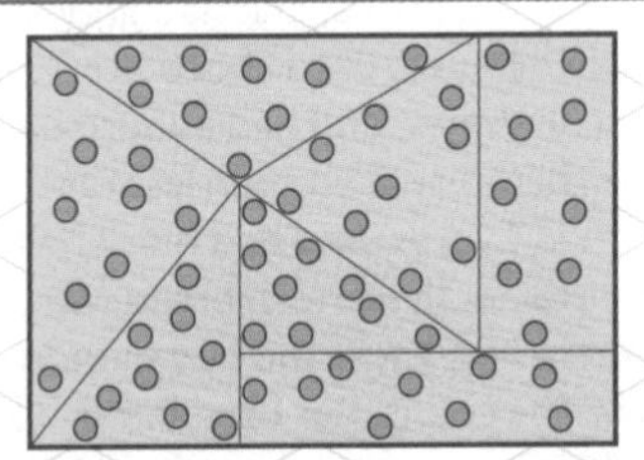

24

28. (Equivalent sectors in both circles sum to a total of 44 to 51, starting from the top right sector.)

25

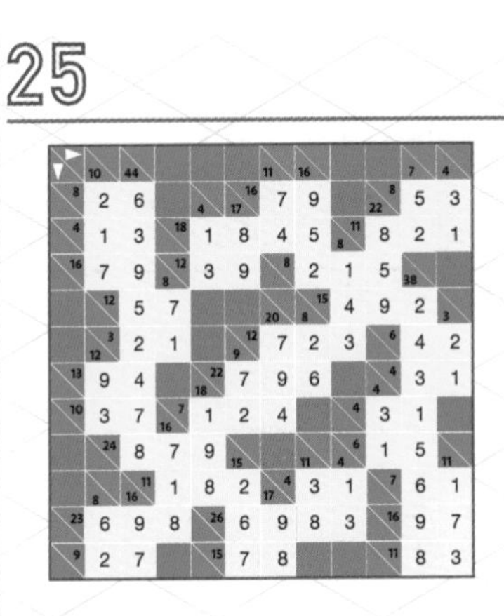

26

A.

27

33. (Equivalent sectors in the second circle are equal to their counterpart in the first circle with the digits reversed and from 2 to 9 subtracted, starting from the top right "12 o'clock" sector.)

28

D & F.

29

Diamond. (Same initial.)

30

2	4	8	9	9	1	7	7	6	9	2
1	5	5	6	0	5	3	8	2	1	7
1	9	2	8	0	7	4	5	0	2	6
2	9	5	7	3	4	3	7	3	3	7
2	2	8	4	6	8	2	9	5	1	3
0	1	3	3	6	5	0	6	6	7	5
8	5	4	6	0	0	7	4	1	4	6
5	8	9	1	5	4	7	2	3	8	2
1	1	6	9	9	6	8	9	9	8	4
4	0	0	0	7	3	1	3	8	0	4

31

17+25-19-15*4-23*8 = 72.

32

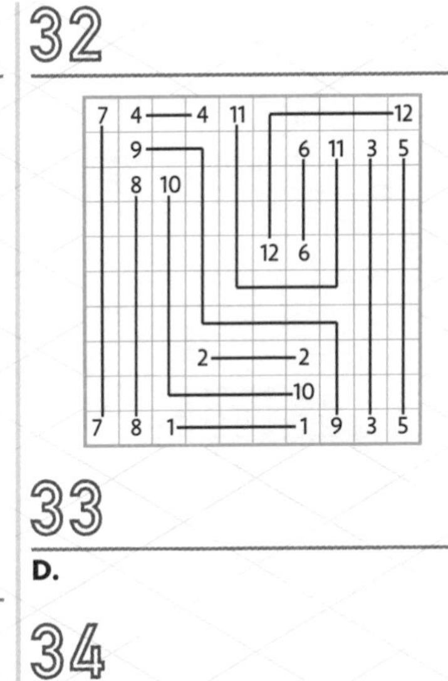

33

D.

34

Lavender. (Third letter of name is same as initial of colour.)

35

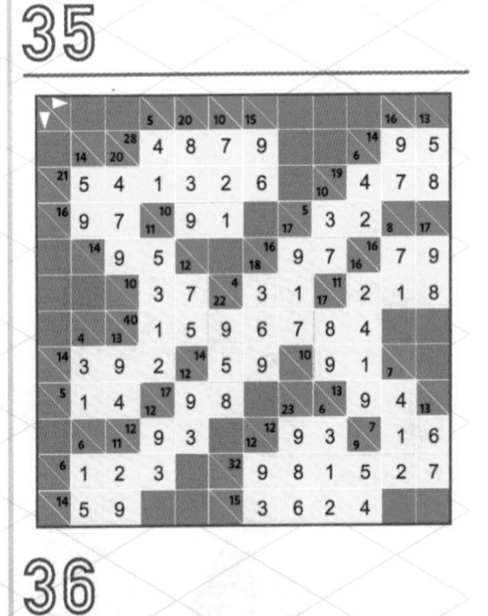

36

9+5-4+5 = 15.

37

i. False (it isn't). **ii. True. iii. False** (he ruled Burkina Faso). **iv. False** (it's Austin). **v. True. vi. True. vii. False** (they were invented in China, 2300 years ago). **viii. True. ix. False** (the columbines). **x. True** (the platypus and four types of echidna).

38

Al Pacino, Jake Gyllenhaal, Will Ferrell, Megan Fox, Samuel L. Jackson, Tom Hanks.

39

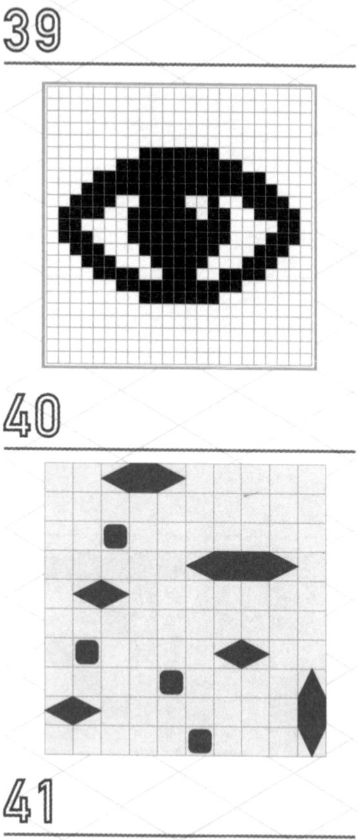

40

41

A triangle.

42

9	9	1	2	0	8	2	1	1	8	6
3	7	4	3	3	7	1	2	0	8	6
6	9	5	6	3	3	4	7	4	4	8
0	1	9	7	7	9	9	9	0	1	4
5	6	3	2	7	8	4	2	0	3	1
6	0	5	5	0	8	6	4	1	9	5
5	5	5	5	7	3	2	0	8	1	8
3	8	2	2	7	2	1	6	1	0	9
6	4	4	7	2	5	4	9	3	7	7
0	0	2	5	6	8	9	8	6	4	3

43

Swallows. (Same length.)

44

(9*7)+(6*5)=63+30 = 93.

45

6	3	7	1	2	5	8	9	4
5	8	2	6	4	9	7	1	3
9	1	4	3	8	7	6	5	2
1	7	5	2	9	4	3	6	8
4	9	3	7	6	8	5	2	1
8	2	6	5	3	1	4	7	9
2	6	1	8	7	3	9	4	5
3	5	9	4	1	6	2	8	7
7	4	8	9	5	2	1	3	6

46

9	5	6	4	2	1	7	8	3
3	7	1	8	5	9	4	2	6
8	2	4	6	7	3	9	5	1
1	6	3	5	4	2	8	7	9
7	4	2	9	1	8	6	3	5
5	9	8	7	3	6	2	1	4
6	1	9	2	8	5	3	4	7
4	8	5	3	6	7	1	9	2
2	3	7	1	9	4	5	6	8

47

▲ = 1, ■ = 3, ● = 4.

48

▶▼	30\	13\			13\	14\	15\		7\	31\	
\8	7	1	6\	\23	8	6	9	13\7	1	6	
\9	6	2	1	19\39	5	8	6	9	4	7	3\
\25	8	3	5	9	11\		\12	4	2	5	1
\16	9	7	\14	6	8	23\			14\11	9	2
			16\10	3	1	6	20\	16\13	9	4	
		17\33	7	1	2	9	6	3	5		
	3\11	2	9		\22	8	9	5		11\	17\
\3	2	1	13\	15\		\7	5	2	13\6	1	5
\16	1	3	4	8	8\	4\	5\20	6	9	3	2
	\22	5	2	7	3	1	4	\7	4	2	1
	\13	6	7	\9	5	3	1		\14	5	9

49

Pierce Brosnan, Macaulay Culkin, Orlando Bloom, Keira Knightley, Emma Stone, Russell Crowe.

50

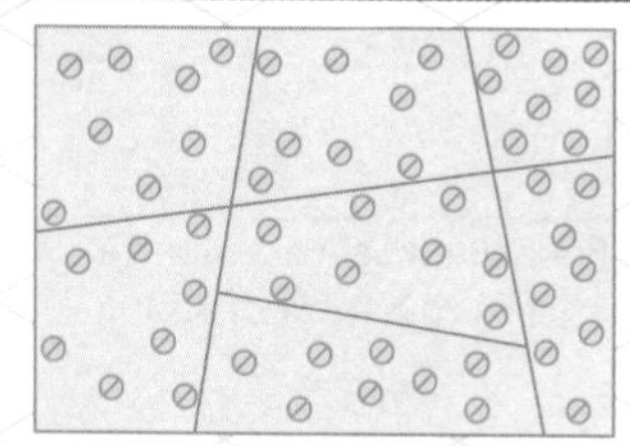

51

i. False (it's in Cygnus). **ii. False** (it was Chile). **iii. True. iv. False** (it's in Belarus). **v. False** (there's also technetium, and most elements with an atomic weight >90). **vi. True. vii. False** (It's a matching card game). **viii. True. ix. False** (it does). **x. True.**

52

Tofu. The teacher liked tofu, was born in California, and had grey hair. The nurse liked chocolate, was born in Wales, and had auburn hair. The therapist liked cherries was born in Cyprus, and had black hair. The trainer liked fresh bread, was born in Provence, and had blonde hair. The counsellor liked lamb, was born in Tuscany, and was bald.

53

Yushan. (If the length of the first name is X, then the Xth letter of the surname is the same as the initial letter of the mountain that the person likes.)

54

54. (The sectors in each circle sum to a total of 114.)

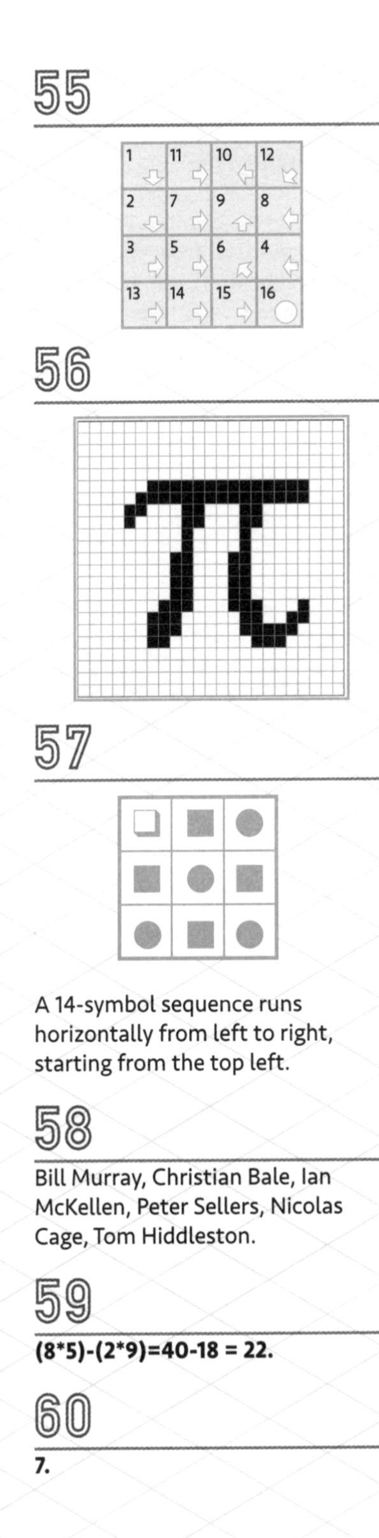

55

56

57

A 14-symbol sequence runs horizontally from left to right, starting from the top left.

58

Bill Murray, Christian Bale, Ian McKellen, Peter Sellers, Nicolas Cage, Tom Hiddleston.

59

(8*5)-(2*9)=40-18 = 22.

60

7.

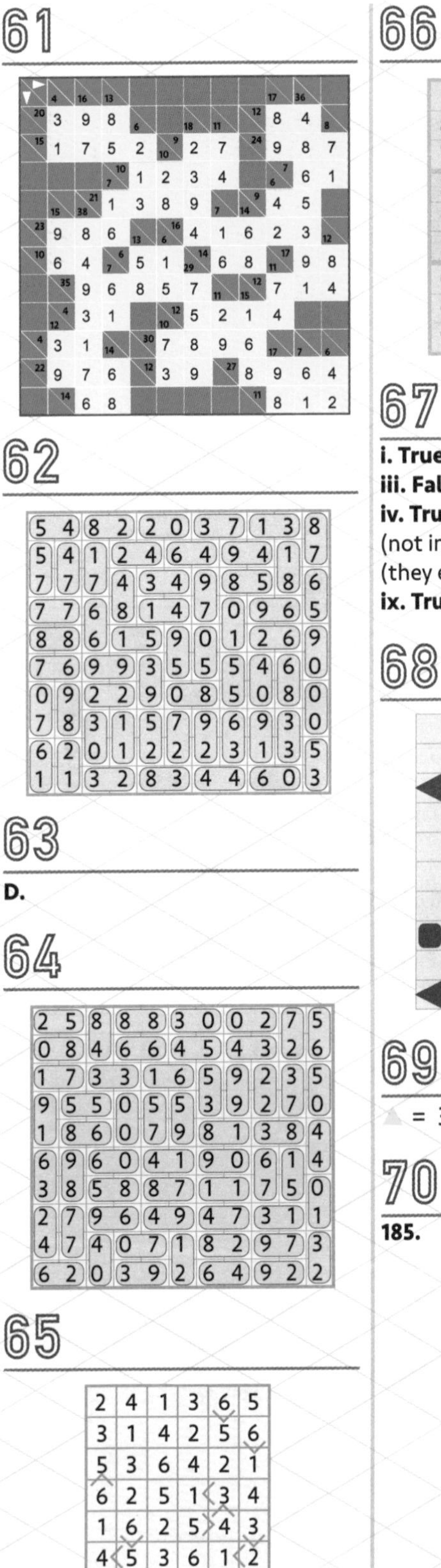

61

62

63

D.

64

65

66

1	4	2	6	7	9	3	8	5
8	9	6	3	4	5	1	7	2
7	3	5	2	1	8	4	9	6
2	1	4	7	9	6	8	5	3
3	7	9	5	8	1	6	2	4
5	6	8	4	3	2	9	1	7
6	5	1	8	2	4	7	3	9
4	8	7	9	5	3	2	6	1
9	2	3	1	6	7	5	4	8

67

i. True. ii. False (Pollux is brighter). **iii. False** (it's a type of solitaire). **iv. True. v. True. vi. True. vii. False** (not in the Americas). **viii. False** (they evolved into the birds). **ix. True. x. False** (it's in Wales).

68

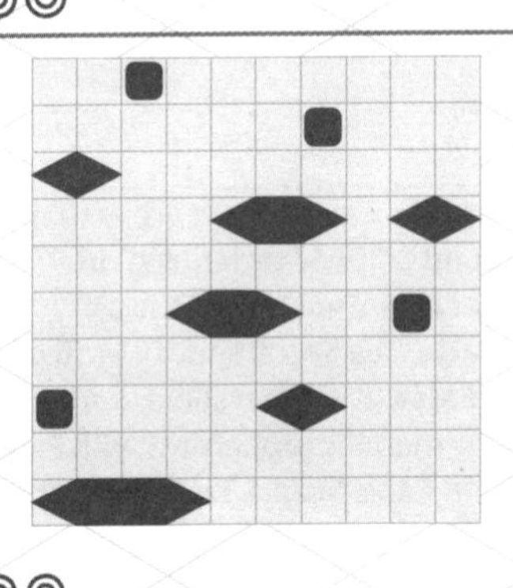

69

▲ = 3, ■ = 4, ● = 7, ★ = 9.

70

185.

71

3	8	1	7	5	2	9	6	4
6	7	5	4	1	9	3	2	8
2	4	9	3	8	6	7	5	1
7	6	8	2	9	4	1	3	5
9	5	3	8	7	1	2	4	6
4	1	2	6	3	5	8	9	7
1	9	7	5	4	3	6	8	2
8	2	4	9	6	7	5	1	3
5	3	6	1	2	8	4	7	9

72

i. False (it's divisible by 3). **ii. True. iii. False** (it was invented in China). **iv. False** (he was a tyrant of Sparta). **v. False** (it's Albany). **vi. False** (it's in Croatia). **vii. True. viii. True. ix. True** (A few know more than a thousand words, and understand the concept of time as expressed by different tenses). **x. True.**

73

i. True. ii. False (there are actually around 8*10^67 orderings). **iii. True. iv. False** (it's in Russia). **v. False** (it's Sacramento). **vi. True. vii. False** (it's a metalloid, with some metallic properties). **viii. False** (it's in Canis Major). **ix. True. x. True.**

74

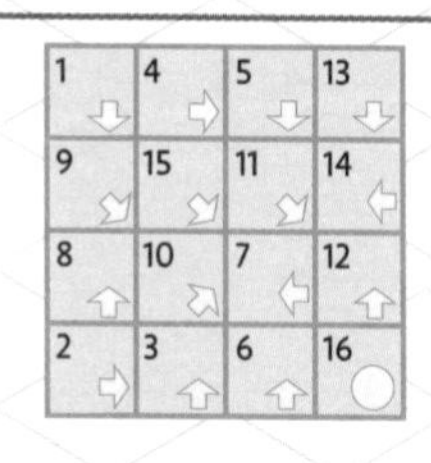

1	4	5	13
9	15	11	14
8	10	7	12
2	3	6	16

75

6th square number = 36.
(Numbers on corners irrelevant.)

76

1	5	2	9	6	7	3	8	4
9	8	6	1	4	3	2	5	7
7	4	3	8	5	2	9	1	6
2	9	5	6	8	4	7	3	1
8	6	7	5	3	1	4	2	9
3	1	4	7	2	9	5	6	8
5	7	8	2	9	6	1	4	3
6	3	9	4	1	5	8	7	2
4	2	1	3	7	8	6	9	5

77

James Franco, Johnny Depp, Kate Beckinsale, Vin Diesel, David Tennant, Angelina Jolie.

78

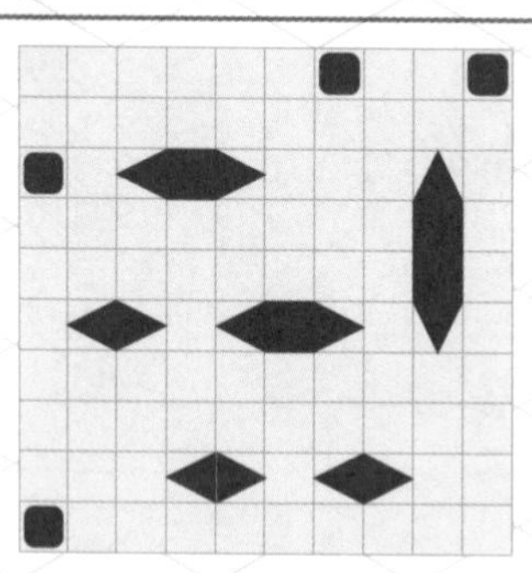

79

0	3	5	8	3	1	9
3	9	8	5	4	9	3
5	8	2	7	0	2	5
8	5	7	9	2	5	3
3	4	0	2	6	4	5
1	9	2	5	4	3	6
9	3	5	3	5	6	1

80

11+5/4*7-23*7-16 = 19.

81

i. False (26AL is radioactive). **ii. False** (Not on Antarctica). **iii. False** (it's Tallahassee). **iv. False** (it was Pakistan). **v. False** (it's irrational). **vi. True. vii. True** (they're called d12s). **viii. True. ix. True. x. False** (It was invented in India).

82

B + H.

83

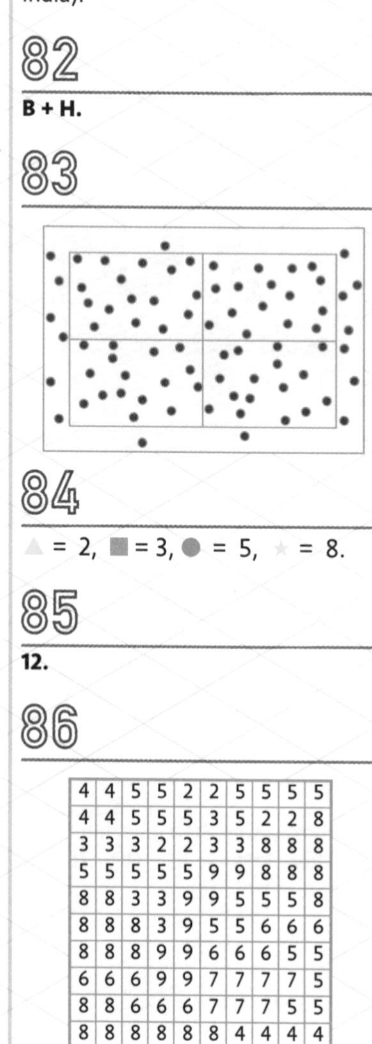

84

▲ = 2, ■ = 3, ● = 5, ★ = 8.

85

12.

86

4	4	5	5	2	2	5	5	5	5
4	4	5	5	5	3	5	2	2	8
3	3	3	2	2	3	3	8	8	8
5	5	5	5	5	9	9	8	8	8
8	8	3	3	9	9	5	5	5	8
8	8	8	3	9	5	5	6	6	6
8	8	8	9	9	6	6	6	5	5
6	6	6	9	9	7	7	7	7	5
8	8	6	6	6	7	7	7	5	5
8	8	8	8	8	8	4	4	4	4

87

1	7	4	8	9	2	5	6	3
6	8	3	5	4	1	9	7	2
2	9	5	7	6	3	1	8	4
8	2	1	3	5	7	4	9	6
9	5	6	1	2	4	7	3	8
4	3	7	9	8	6	2	5	1
5	6	8	2	1	9	3	4	7
3	4	2	6	7	5	8	1	9
7	1	9	4	3	8	6	2	5

88

20. (Diagonally opposing pairs of sectors in each circle sum to a total of 23.)

89

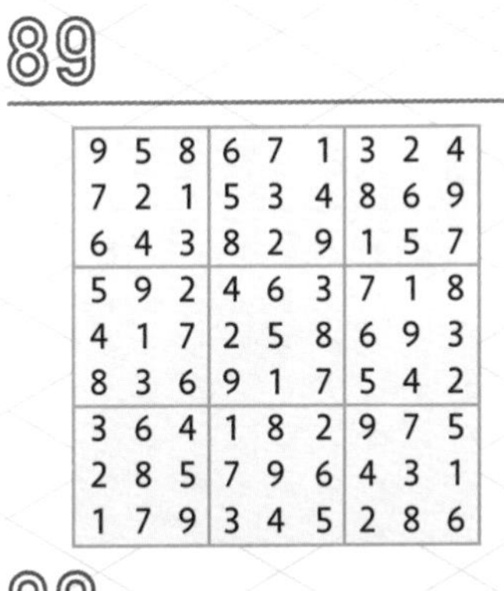

9	5	8	6	7	1	3	2	4
7	2	1	5	3	4	8	6	9
6	4	3	8	2	9	1	5	7
5	9	2	4	6	3	7	1	8
4	1	7	2	5	8	6	9	3
8	3	6	9	1	7	5	4	2
3	6	4	1	8	2	9	7	5
2	8	5	7	9	6	4	3	1
1	7	9	3	4	5	2	8	6

90

A 17-symbol sequence runs horizontally from left to right, starting from the top left.

91

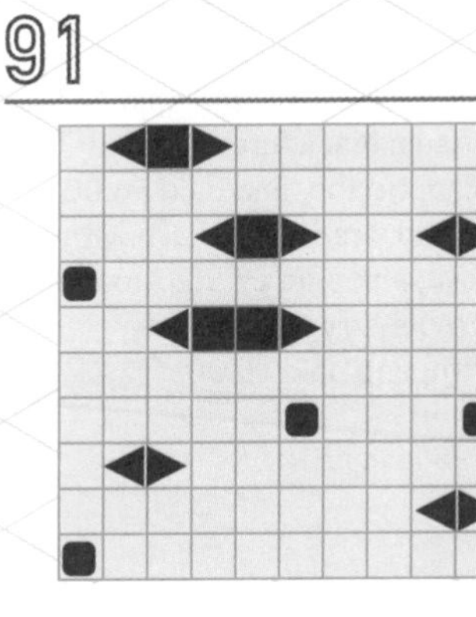

92

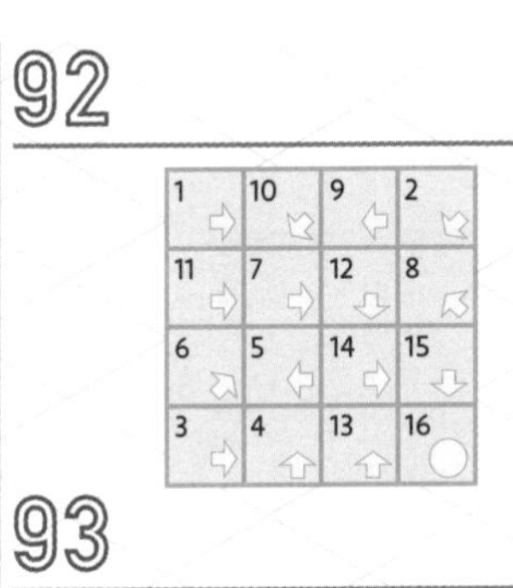

93

C.

94

Rupert Grint, Edward Norton, Jack Nicholson, Channing Tatum, Bruce Willis, James McAvoy.

95

▲ = 1, ■ = 2, ● = 3, ★ = 5.

96

A rectangle.

97

5	2	7	4	1	9	6	8	3
4	8	3	2	6	7	9	1	5
6	1	9	5	3	8	4	2	7
3	5	6	9	2	1	7	4	8
8	9	4	7	5	6	1	3	2
1	7	2	8	4	3	5	6	9
9	4	1	3	8	5	2	7	6
7	6	8	1	9	2	3	5	4
2	3	5	6	7	4	8	9	1

98

A star.

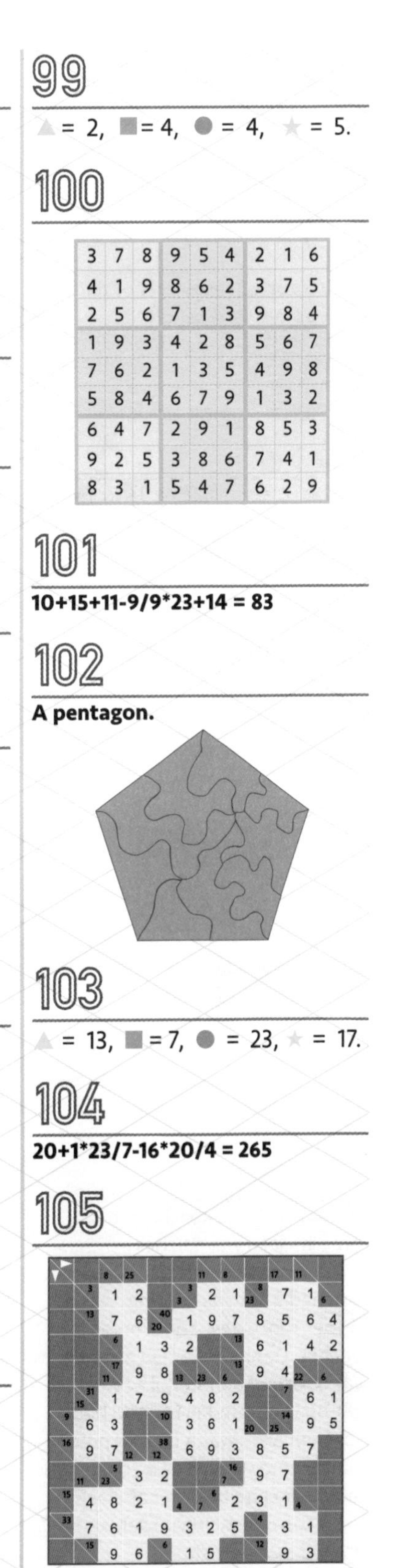

99

▲ = 2, ■ = 4, ● = 4, ★ = 5.

100

3	7	8	9	5	4	2	1	6
4	1	9	8	6	2	3	7	5
2	5	6	7	1	3	9	8	4
1	9	3	4	2	8	5	6	7
7	6	2	1	3	5	4	9	8
5	8	4	6	7	9	1	3	2
6	4	7	2	9	1	8	5	3
9	2	5	3	8	6	7	4	1
8	3	1	5	4	7	6	2	9

101

10+15+11-9/9*23+14 = 83

102

A pentagon.

103

▲ = 13, ■ = 7, ● = 23, ★ = 17.

104

20+1*23/7-16*20/4 = 265

105

106

43. Two largest numbers multiplied – two smallest numbers multiplied = (9*7)-(4*5)=63-20 = 43.

107

Sonic Youth. (Last letter of name is same as initial of band.)

108

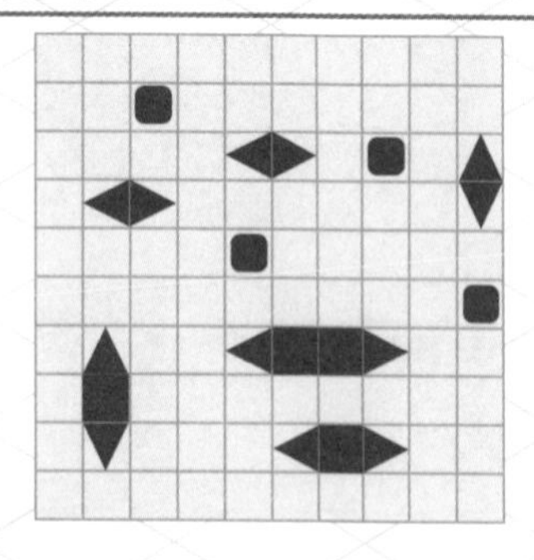

109

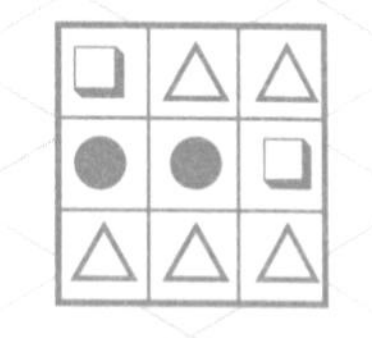

A 13-symbol sequence runs horizontally backwards from right to left, starting from the bottom right. Each time a new row is started, 5 symbols from the sequence are skipped.

110

Gymnastics. Elizabeth, who had a forearm scar, was former gymnast, and worked as a librarian. Rebecca, who had a torn hamstring, was a former footballer, and worked as a teacher. Daniel, who had a sprain, was a former sprinter, and worked as a pharmacist. Kevin, who had a broken arm, was a former pole vaulter, and worked as a cook. Kelly, who had been in car crash, was a former snowboarder, and worked as a barrista.

111

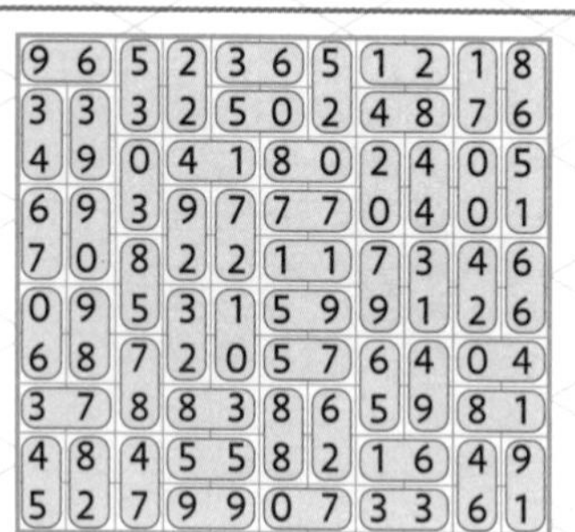

112

42.5.

113

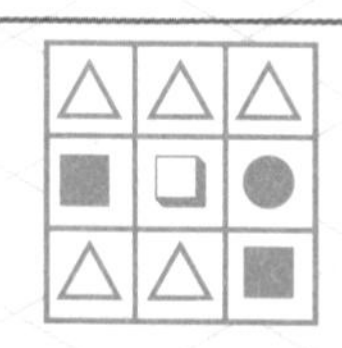

A 13-symbol sequence runs vertically from top to bottom, starting from the top left.

114

5	7	0	3	4	7	4
7	0	4	5	8	4	3
0	4	6	9	6	1	5
3	5	9	7	9	8	6
4	8	6	9	2	3	9
7	4	1	8	3	5	6
4	3	5	6	9	6	1

115

(9*1)-7 = 2.

116

130.

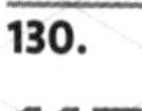

117

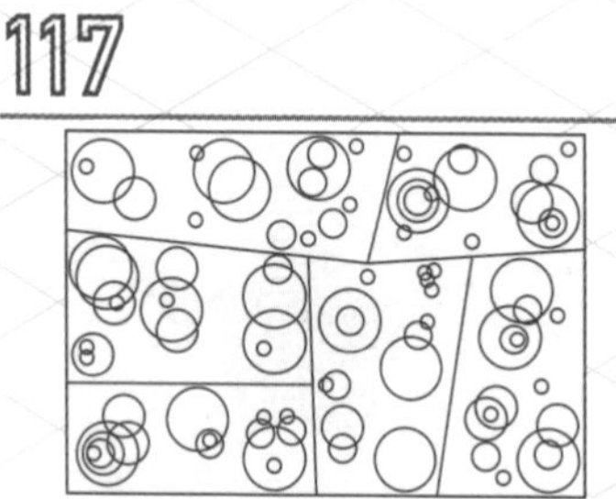

118

i. True. ii. False (they have four). **iii. True. iv. False** (they're used to wrap a cheese). **v. False** (it's in Spain). **vi. True. vii. True. viii. True. ix. True. x. True.**

119

A 12-symbol sequence spirals inwardly clockwise, starting from the top left.

120

8	5	3	6	9	1	2	4	7
9	2	4	7	3	5	1	6	8
6	1	7	4	2	8	5	9	3
4	8	6	2	5	7	9	3	1
2	7	9	1	6	3	4	8	5
1	3	5	8	4	9	6	7	2
3	4	1	5	8	6	7	2	9
5	6	8	9	7	2	3	1	4
7	9	2	3	1	4	8	5	6

121

A.

122

Cappuccino. Richard had a croissant with an americano, and paid £4.00. Scott had a pain au chocolat with latte, and paid £4.50. Mary had a black forest gateau with cappuccino, and paid £6.00. Jeffrey had a red velvet cake with an espresso, and paid £5.50. Amanda had a blueberry muffin with ristretto, and paid £5.00.

123

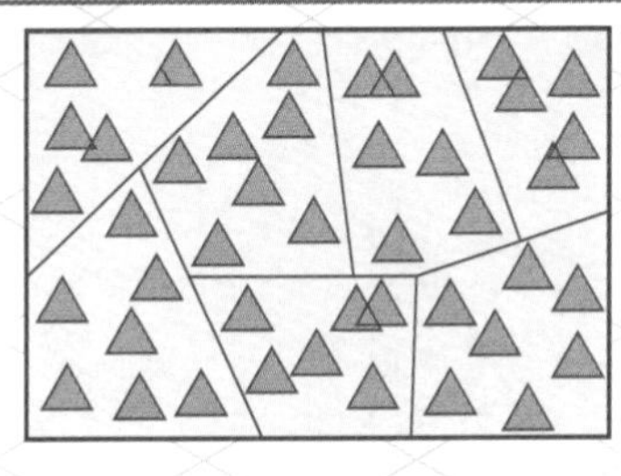

124

14. (The top two and bottom two sectors in each circle sum to the same value as the left two and right two sectors, 60.)

125

A.

126

Ben Stiller, Matt Damon, Owen Wilson, Anne Hathaway, Tim Allen, Robin Williams.

127

1	2	5	1	9	4	2
2	9	4	7	3	9	3
5	4	8	9	4	6	1
1	7	9	5	8	1	2
9	3	4	8	0	5	4
4	9	6	1	5	2	9
2	3	1	2	4	9	1

128

3	2	1	5	6	4
1	5	6	4	3	2
6	3	2	1	4	5
5	6	4	2	1	3
2	4	3	6	5	1
4	1	5	3	2	6

129

11. (11+4)-(3+7)=5.

130

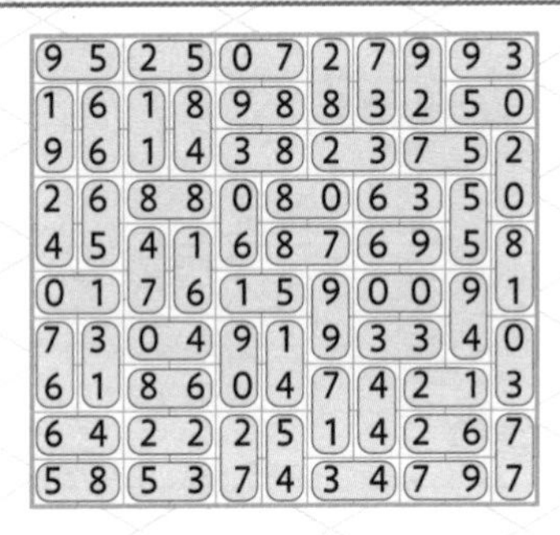

9	5	2	5	0	7	2	7	9	9	3
1	6	1	8	9	8	8	3	2	5	0
9	6	1	4	3	8	2	3	7	5	2
2	6	8	8	0	8	0	6	3	5	0
4	5	4	1	6	8	7	6	9	5	8
0	1	7	6	1	5	9	0	0	9	1
7	3	0	4	9	1	9	3	3	4	0
6	1	8	6	0	4	7	4	2	1	3
6	4	2	2	2	5	1	4	2	6	7
5	8	5	3	7	4	3	4	7	9	7

131

5	6	2	4	3	1
2	3	5	1	6	4
3	2	1	5	4	6
1	4	3	6	5	2
4	5	6	2	1	3
6	1	4	3	2	5

132

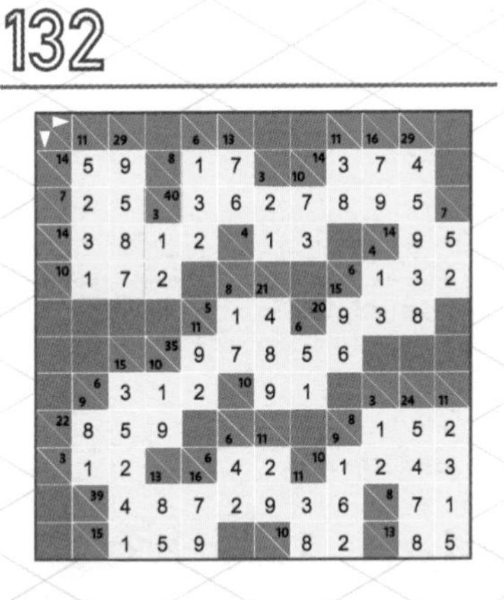

133

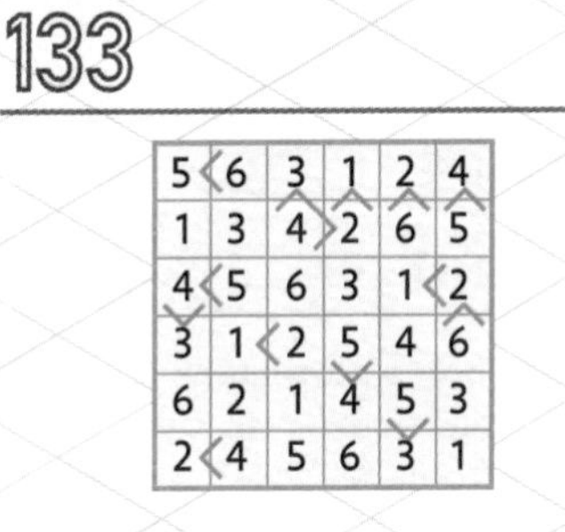

5	6	3	1	2	4
1	3	4	2	6	5
4	5	6	3	1	2
3	1	2	5	4	6
6	2	1	4	5	3
2	4	5	6	3	1

134

Everton. (4th letter of name is same as last letter of football club.)

135

50. (Equivalent sectors in both circles sum to a total of 31, 37, 41, 43, 47, 53, 59 and 61, the primes >29 in ascending order, starting from the top right "12 o'clock" sector.)

136

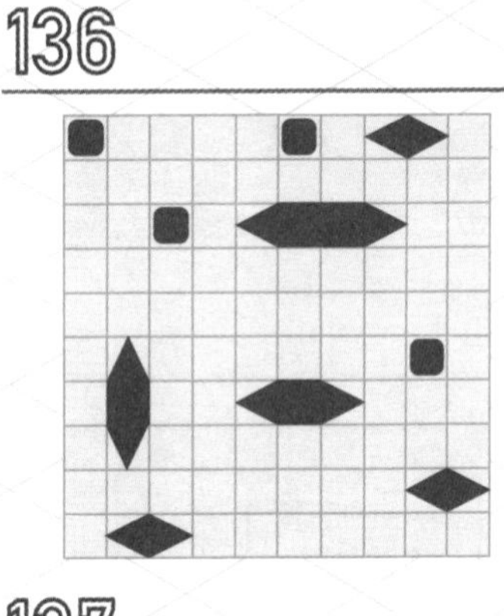

137

A hexagon.

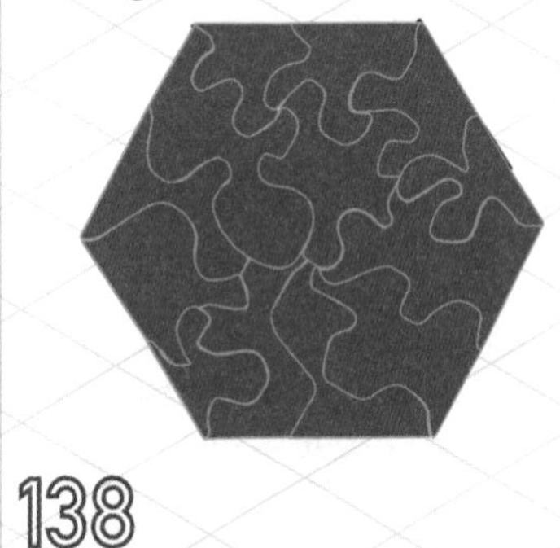

138

13. (Diagonally opposing pairs of sectors and their equivalent sectors in the second circle collectively sum to a total of 57.)

139

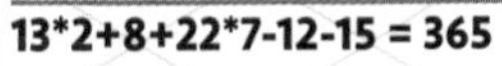

13*2+8+22*7-12-15 = 365

140

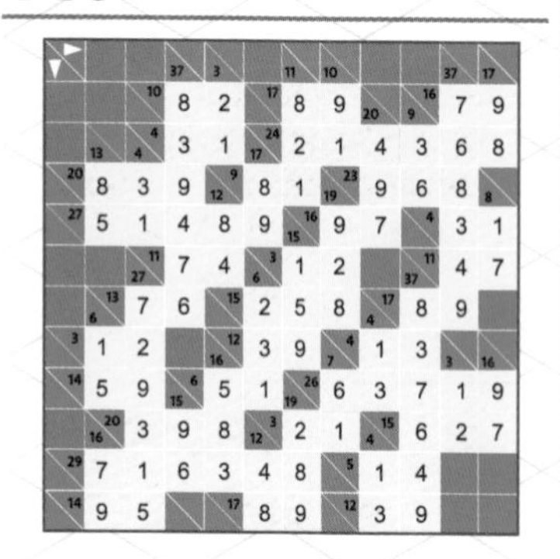

141

142

i. False (it's third, twice as abundant as steam). **ii. False** (they don't). **iii. True. iv. True. v. False** (they belong to many other genera as well). **vi. True. vii. False** (it's a peacock; the constellation that represents a phoenix is, well, Phoenix). **viii. False** (it was invented in Germany). **ix. True. x. False** (it uses five dice).

143

A 17-symbol sequence runs vertically from the bottom right and retreats leftwards, changing from upwards to downwards at the end of each line.

144

2	4	5	7	0	3	8
4	5	4	8	2	1	4
5	4	1	9	3	8	0
7	8	9	1	8	7	9
0	2	3	8	7	2	4
3	1	8	7	2	7	8
8	4	0	9	4	8	3

145

Moscow. (People whose names start with vowels like capital cities.)

146

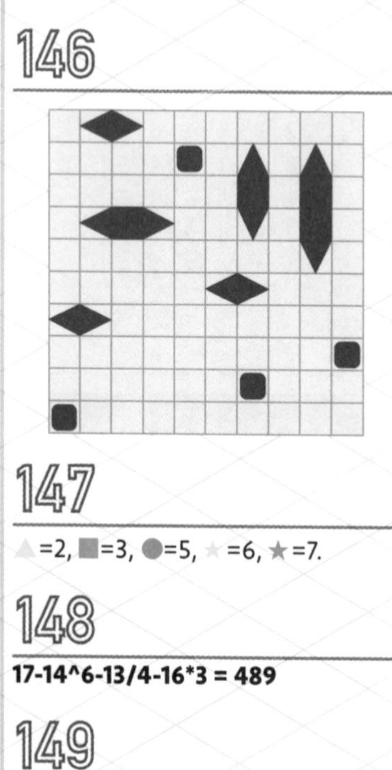

147

▲=2, ■=3, ●=5, ★=6, ★=7.

148

17-14^6-13/4-16*3 = 489

149

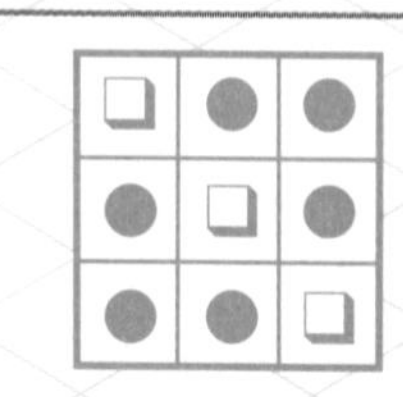

A 17-symbol sequence runs horizontally from left to right, starting from the top left and jumping every other line to the bottom half of the table, starting from the ninth row, so that the rows run in the order 1, 9, 2, 10, ... 15, 8.

150

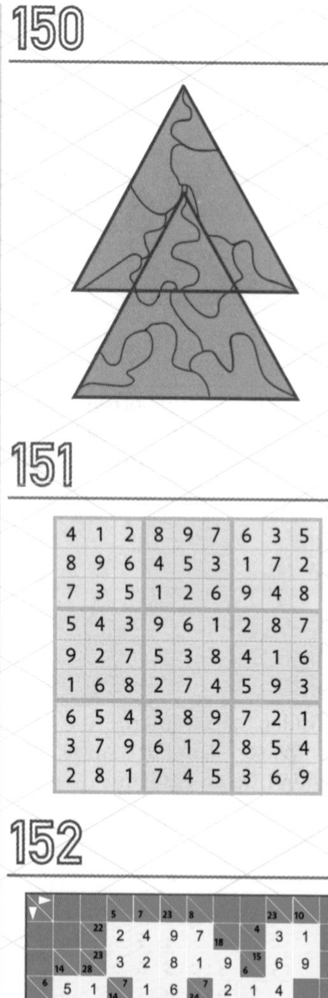

151

4	1	2	8	9	7	6	3	5
8	9	6	4	5	3	1	7	2
7	3	5	1	2	6	9	4	8
5	4	3	9	6	1	2	8	7
9	2	7	5	3	8	4	1	6
1	6	8	2	7	4	5	9	3
6	5	4	3	8	9	7	2	1
3	7	9	6	1	2	8	5	4
2	8	1	7	4	5	3	6	9

152

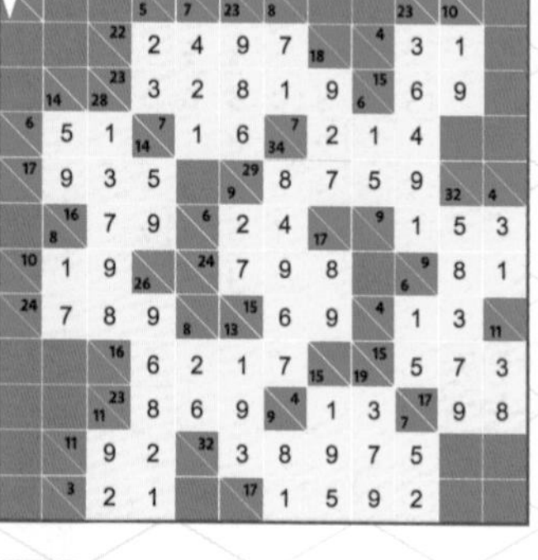

153

4	1	3	5	2	6
5	4	2	6	3	1
2	5	4	1	6	3
6	3	5	2	1	4
3	6	1	4	5	2
1	2	6	3	4	5

154

E (right) **& G** (top).

155

5	3	3	5	9	2	0	7	4	1	4
6	4	6	9	5	8	2	1	4	6	4
7	1	8	7	2	2	7	3	5	6	9
8	6	8	3	2	0	0	1	5	9	4
8	8	2	0	8	9	6	2	5	3	2
3	5	7	4	6	0	6	2	3	9	7
3	0	9	1	9	3	1	3	6	6	1
5	0	4	1	0	6	8	0	7	3	8
2	7	7	0	1	0	4	7	4	8	2
5	1	7	5	9	1	4	5	9	9	8

156

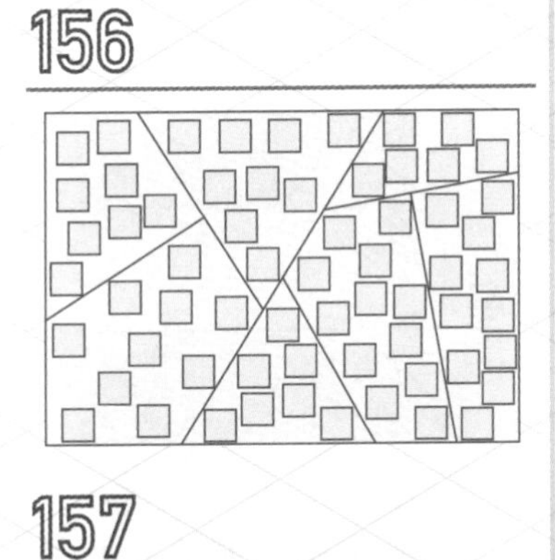

157

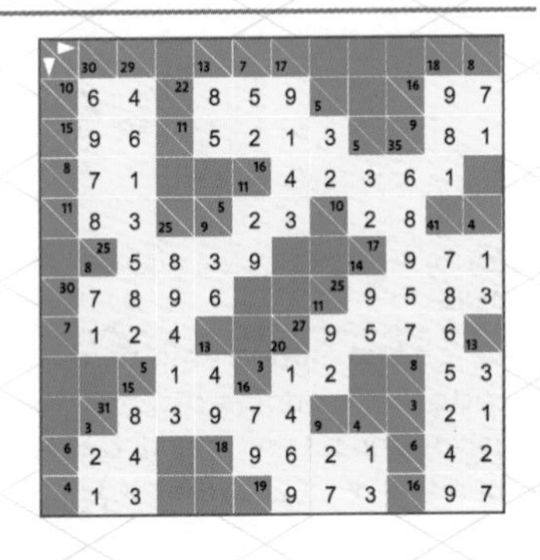

158

Albuquerque. In sequential order: **1.** Mark, a Derry taxi driver, who drove a Lexus, and used worms. **2.** Julie, a Portland manager, who drove a Ford, and used a crankbait. **3.** Laura, a Tulsa singer, who drove a Toyota, and used a spinnerbait. **4.** Sarah, an Albuquerque rancher, who drove a Chevrolet, and used a jig. **5.** Steven, a Chicago secretary, who drove a Tesla, and used a spoon lure.

159

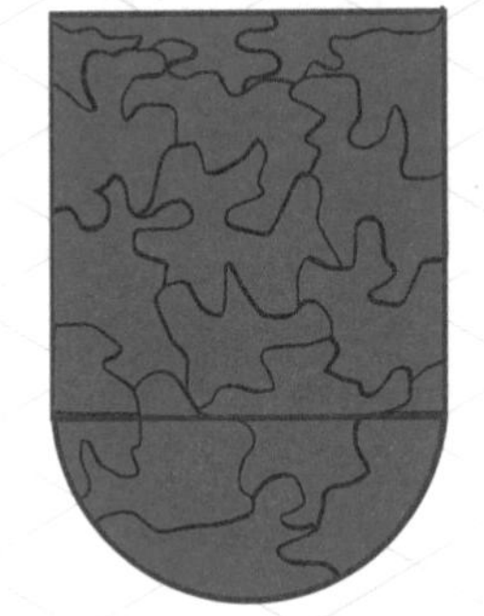

160

1	10	9	5
3	8	6	4
2	7	12	13
15	11	14	16

161

7^3-(17*13)=343-221 = 122.

162

i. True. ii. False (it's colourless). **iii. False** (It comes from Latin America). **iv. True** (it's in Hampshire). **v. False** (they can also include 1s). **vi. True. vii. False** (it's Salem). **viii. True. ix. False** (it represents sails; the constellation that represents a herdsman is Boötes). **x. True.**

163

3	2	5	1	3	6	2
2	1	4	7	2	3	5
5	4	7	8	1	4	8
1	7	8	2	3	5	1
3	2	1	3	3	0	2
6	3	4	5	0	1	4
2	5	8	1	2	4	5

164

Julia Roberts, Steve Buscemi, Tommy Lee Jones, Rachel McAdams, Bruce Springsteen, Jackie Chan.

165

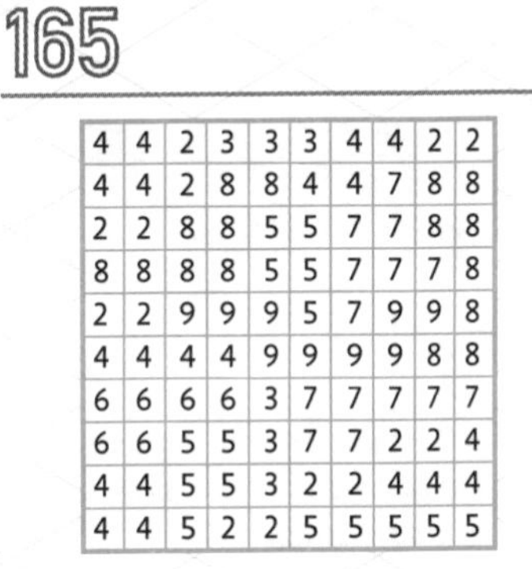

4	4	2	3	3	3	4	4	2	2
4	4	2	8	8	4	4	7	8	8
2	2	8	8	5	5	7	7	8	8
8	8	8	8	5	5	7	7	7	8
2	2	9	9	9	5	7	9	9	8
4	4	4	4	9	9	9	9	8	8
6	6	6	6	3	7	7	7	7	7
6	6	5	5	3	7	7	2	2	4
4	4	5	5	3	2	2	4	4	4
4	4	5	2	2	5	5	5	5	5

166

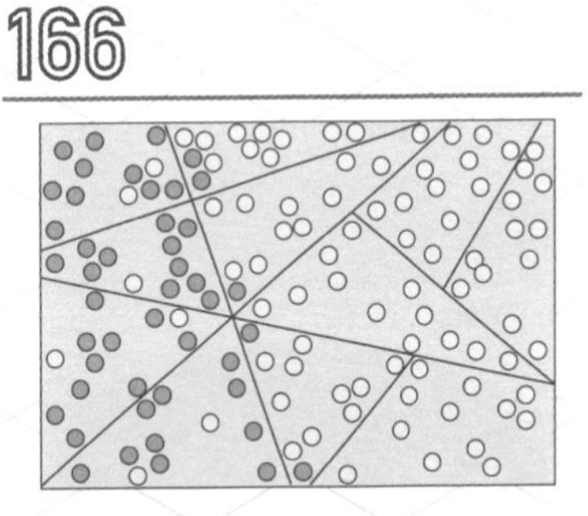

167

1	9	14	13
8	4	10	12
3	7	5	11
2	6	15	16

168

4	4	7	7	9	9	9	6	6	6
4	4	7	7	9	9	9	6	6	6
2	2	7	7	7	9	9	9	4	4
6	6	6	6	6	6	8	8	4	4
5	5	8	8	8	8	8	8	3	3
5	5	5	3	3	3	6	6	6	3
3	3	3	4	4	4	4	6	6	6
2	2	9	9	9	9	9	9	9	9
4	4	4	5	5	5	5	2	2	9
4	2	2	5	2	2	4	4	4	4

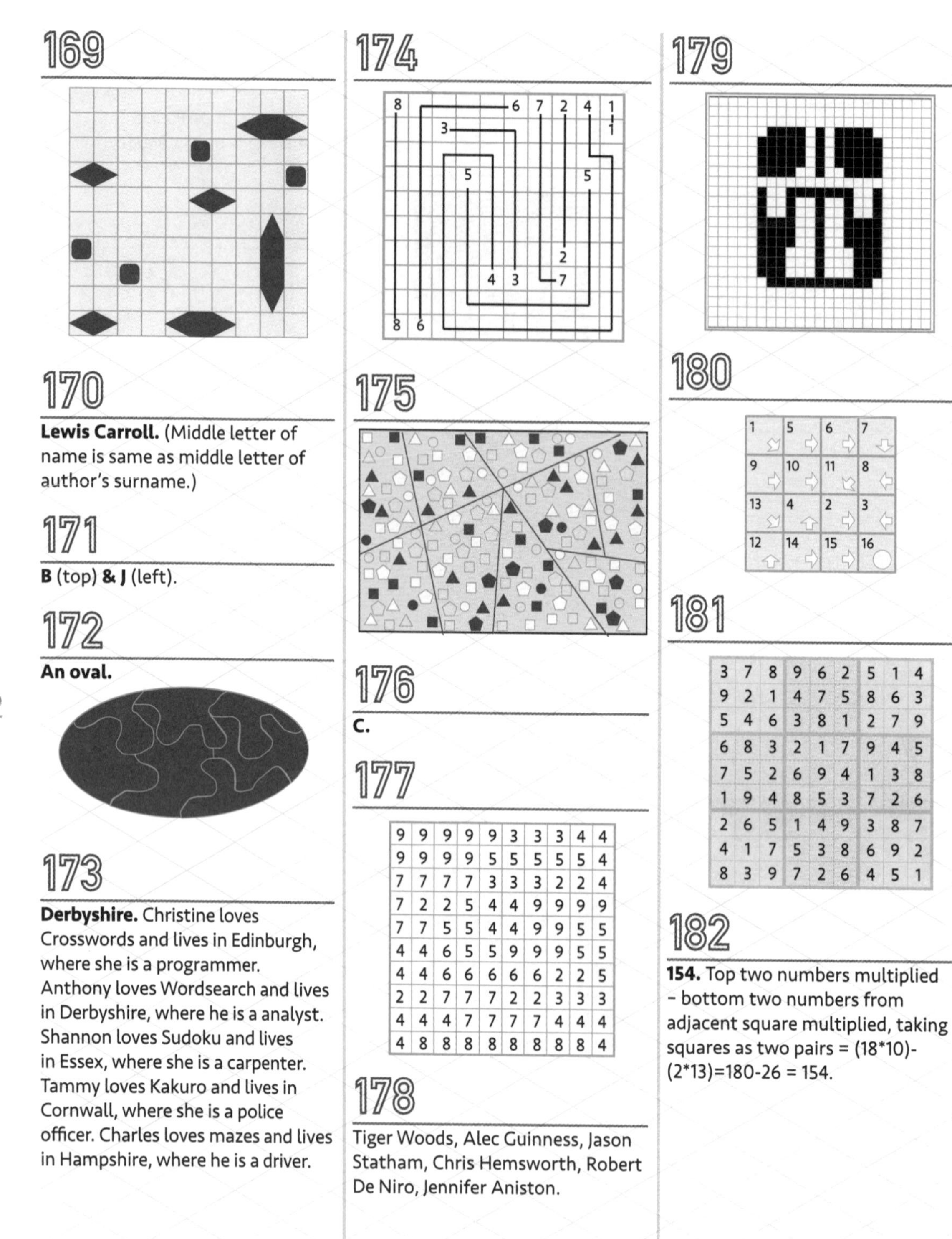

169

170

Lewis Carroll. (Middle letter of name is same as middle letter of author's surname.)

171

B (top) **& J** (left).

172

An oval.

173

Derbyshire. Christine loves Crosswords and lives in Edinburgh, where she is a programmer. Anthony loves Wordsearch and lives in Derbyshire, where he is a analyst. Shannon loves Sudoku and lives in Essex, where she is a carpenter. Tammy loves Kakuro and lives in Cornwall, where she is a police officer. Charles loves mazes and lives in Hampshire, where he is a driver.

174

175

176

C.

177

9	9	9	9	9	3	3	3	4	4
9	9	9	9	5	5	5	5	5	4
7	7	7	7	3	3	3	2	2	4
7	2	2	5	4	4	9	9	9	9
7	7	5	5	4	4	9	9	5	5
4	4	6	5	5	9	9	9	5	5
4	4	6	6	6	6	6	2	2	5
2	2	7	7	7	2	2	3	3	3
4	4	4	7	7	7	7	4	4	4
4	8	8	8	8	8	8	8	8	4

178

Tiger Woods, Alec Guinness, Jason Statham, Chris Hemsworth, Robert De Niro, Jennifer Aniston.

179

180

1	5	6	7
9	10	11	8
13	4	2	3
12	14	15	16

181

3	7	8	9	6	2	5	1	4
9	2	1	4	7	5	8	6	3
5	4	6	3	8	1	2	7	9
6	8	3	2	1	7	9	4	5
7	5	2	6	9	4	1	3	8
1	9	4	8	5	3	7	2	6
2	6	5	1	4	9	3	8	7
4	1	7	5	3	8	6	9	2
8	3	9	7	2	6	4	5	1

182

154. Top two numbers multiplied – bottom two numbers from adjacent square multiplied, taking squares as two pairs = (18*10)-(2*13)=180-26 = 154.

183

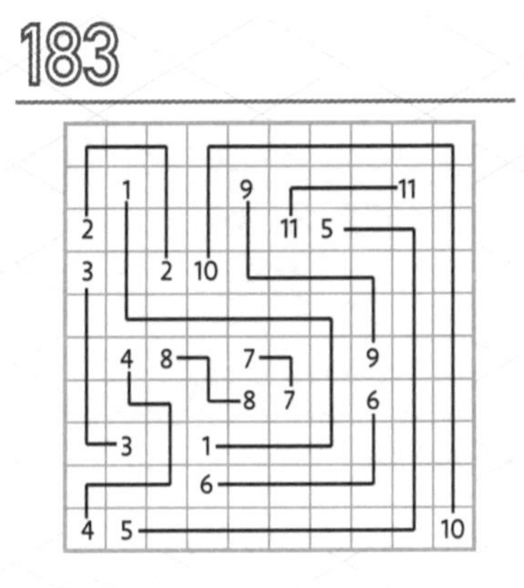

184

25*9/10+1*14-11-19*1 = 299

185

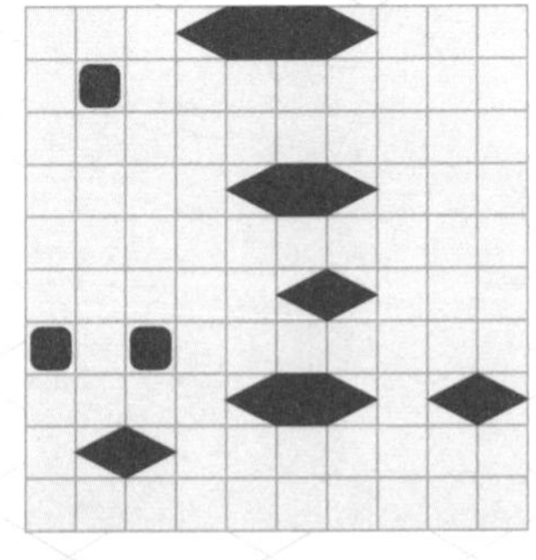

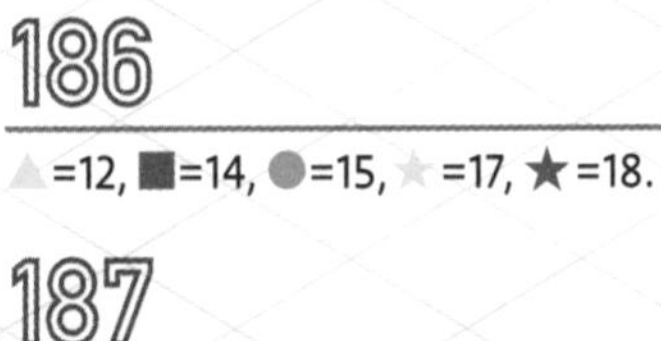

186

▲=12, ■=14, ●=15, ★=17, ★=18.

187

5+16-20^3+25*11/2-25*8 = 944

188

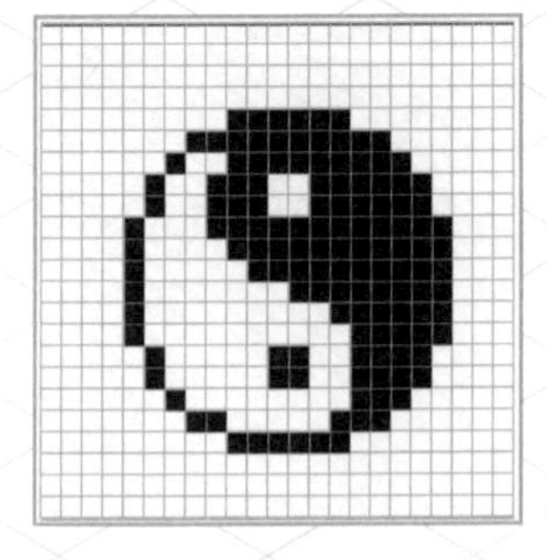

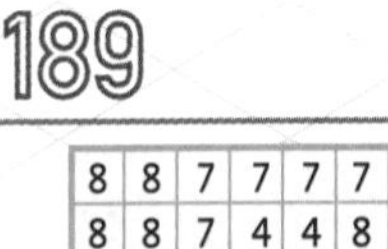

189

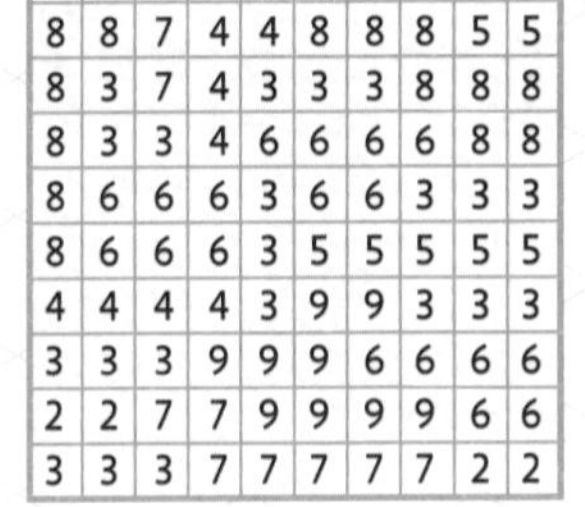

8	8	7	7	7	7	7	5	5	5
8	8	7	4	4	8	8	8	5	5
8	3	7	4	3	3	3	8	8	8
8	3	3	4	6	6	6	6	8	8
8	6	6	6	3	6	6	3	3	3
8	6	6	6	3	5	5	5	5	5
4	4	4	4	3	9	9	3	3	3
3	3	3	9	9	9	6	6	6	6
2	2	7	7	9	9	9	9	6	6
3	3	3	7	7	7	7	7	2	2

190

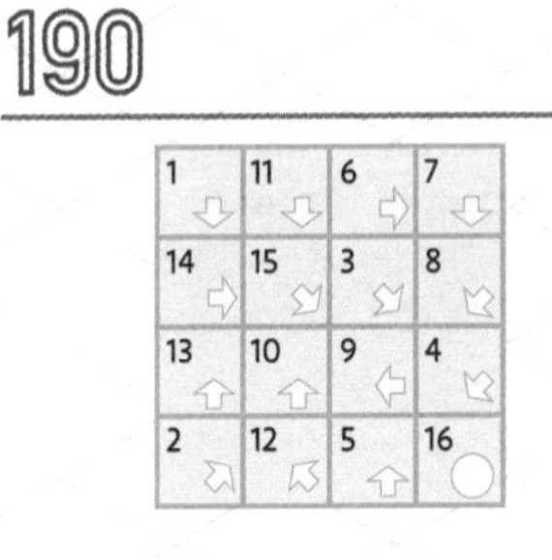

191

Tanya. Tanya had a sausage sandwich and a red sweater, and liked Bobtail cats. Joshua had a brie sandwich and a green sweater, and liked Shorthair cats. Ryan had a omelette sandwich and a mauve sweater, and liked Siamese cats. Jeremy had a turkey sandwich and a white sweater, and liked Persian cats. Lucy had a cheddar sandwich and a blue sweater, and liked Manx cats.)

192

Jessica Alba, Kevin Spacey, Clint Eastwood, Drew Barrymore, Rowan Atkinson, Kate Winslet.

193

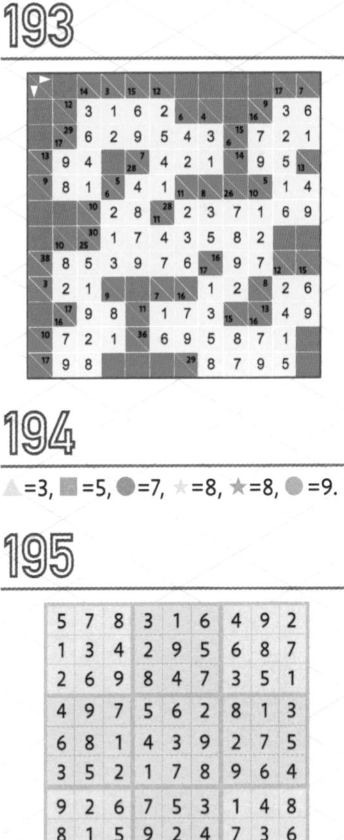

194

▲=3, ■=5, ●=7, ★=8, ★=8, ●=9.

195

5	7	8	3	1	6	4	9	2
1	3	4	2	9	5	6	8	7
2	6	9	8	4	7	3	5	1
4	9	7	5	6	2	8	1	3
6	8	1	4	3	9	2	7	5
3	5	2	1	7	8	9	6	4
9	2	6	7	5	3	1	4	8
8	1	5	9	2	4	7	3	6
7	4	3	6	8	1	5	2	9

196

Cumbria. The first interviewee was Tina from Hampshire, a writer with black hair, who wanted to adopt a labrador. The second interviewee was Patricia from Powys, an optician with blonde hair, who wanted to adopt a poodle. The third interviewee was Lori from Norfolk, a chef with red hair, who wanted to adopt a spaniel. The fourth interviewee was Gregory from Cumbria, a professor with brown hair, who wanted to adopt a terrier. The fifth interviewee was Kenneth from Strathclyde, a marketer with grey hair, who wanted to adopt a corgi.

TH 414/1 #8

197

1	5	9	4	6	2	3	7	8
8	4	6	3	9	7	5	1	2
7	2	3	8	1	5	6	4	9
5	7	2	9	4	3	1	8	6
9	3	8	6	2	1	7	5	4
4	6	1	5	7	8	9	2	3
2	9	4	1	5	6	8	3	7
6	8	5	7	3	4	2	9	1
3	1	7	2	8	9	4	6	5

198

27. (The numbers across both circles form a sequence, starting from 20, that runs +7, -12, +3, and that switches back and forth from circle to circle, starting from the top right "12 o'clock" sector, going from first circle to the mirrored equivalent sector in the second circle, then progressing clockwise one space back in the first circle.)

199

Bristol. (The numeric position of the last letter of the first name is equal to the length of the car marque that the person likes.)

200

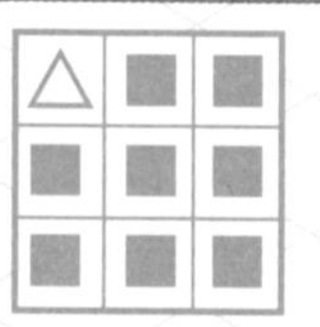

A 19-symbol sequence spirals inwardly clockwise, starting from the bottom left.

SCORE

Newport Community
Learning & Libraries